Agriculture in the United Kingdom 2002: errata

0 11 243070 8

G000114627

Errata   The following changes have been made to Agriculture in the U

- Page 11, paragraph 27: Average net farm income in the UK increased by 20 per cent between 2000/01 and 2001/02, and not by 19 per cent.

- Page 11, paragraph 28: Average UK net farm income peaked in 1995/96 at £39,300, and not at £39,200.

- Page 11, paragraph 30: Average net farm income in 2002/03 is forecast to increase by 24 per cent, and not by 30 per cent.

- Page 18, Table 2.7 Net farm income by country and type of farm: This table has been revised substantially, and is shown in full overleaf.

- Page 28, Table 3.5 Labour force in agriculture: The data for this table is shown in units of thousand persons. Footnote (i) is missing; it reads 'Figures exclude schoolchildren and most trainees'.

- Page 66, Table 5.18 Milk products: The provisional figure of 6 thousand tonnes for the production of cheese in 2000 should read 396 thousand tonnes.

- Page 100, Table 8.1 Payments and levies in the production and income account: The figure of £129 million for 'Total subsidies (less levies) on product' in 2000 should read £2,187 million.

- Page 121, Chart 10.3 Key bird populations: This is replaced by the chart below:

Chart 10.3 Key bird populations

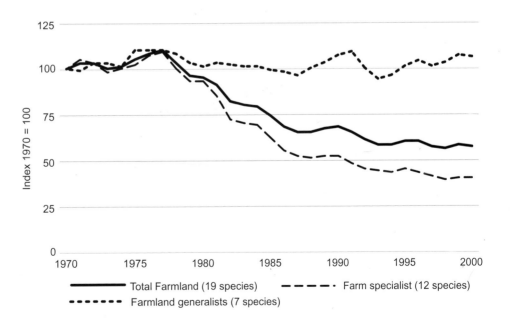

Table 2.7 Net Farm Income by country and type of farm

Inquiries: Sophie Cruickshank 020 7238 3268 email: sophie.cruickshank@defra.gsi.gov.uk

Average net farm income per farm (£ thousand/farm)   Accounting years ending on average in February

	1994/95	1995/96	1996/97	1997/98	1998/99	1999/00	2000/01	2001/02 (a)	2002/03 (provisional) (a)
At current prices									
England									
dairy	36.3	41.1	33.6	22.0	13.5	9.0	10.8	22.8	17.0
cattle and sheep (LFA) (b)	13.1	17.2	17.4	10.7	5.7	4.6	6.7	9.7	25.0
cattle and sheep (lowland)	10.4	10.8	9.5	1.1	0.9	0.6	-0.4	-0.5	8.0
cereals	31.7	49.6	43.9	16.8	8.9	13.5	7.3	4.1	9.5
general cropping	72.2	89.1	47.6	23.1	36.0	8.8	18.4	17.9	17.5
pigs and poultry	31.5	67.3	60.9	20.4	-15.8	-5.3	37.9	21.8	30.0
mixed	34.2	51.8	39.6	8.9	1.6	9.4	9.7	5.5	15.5
Wales									
dairy	29.7	51.8	45.8	32.9	18.5	18.2	15.4	29.6	21.5
cattle and sheep (LFA) (b)	5.6	16.1	12.6	7.6	3.6	2.5	3.0	1.7	6.0
cattle and sheep (lowland)	6.1	12.4	8.9	2.3	-0.9	0.4	0.5	2.2	6.5
Scotland									
dairy	38.0	45.7	39.2	17.4	5.6	1.8	13.9	33.1	41.5
cattle and sheep (LFA) (b)	12.7	14.6	18.4	8.0	4.7	2.7	5.6	5.8	11.0
cereals	42.0	72.5	71.8	1.5	0.6	27.2	4.0	-0.6	-7.5
general cropping	29.6	26.6	11.7	-	10.3	2.2	5.1	8.0	-2.5
mixed	23.7	31.3	26.1	-3.8	2.0	5.3	6.6	12.6	20.5
Northern Ireland									
dairy	23.2	32.1	20.8	11.8	8.6	8.3	14.9	17.5	10.5
cattle and sheep (LFA) (b)	5.6	6.6	6.8	3.5	0.3	-1.8	0.9	4.0	2.5
United Kingdom									
dairy	33.7	41.3	33.4	21.3	12.8	9.5	12.4	23.2	17.5
cattle and sheep (LFA) (b)	7.9	12.3	12.2	6.5	3.2	2.0	3.8	4.8	10.0
cattle and sheep (lowland)	7.9	8.6	7.0	0.7	-0.2	-	-	0.4	7.5
cereals	33.9	53.5	47.7	16.3	8.3	13.1	6.8	3.3	7.0
general cropping	74.7	87.3	45.2	19.8	34.7	7.8	18.8	15.7	13.0
pigs and poultry	26.7	56.8	51.5	17.6	-17.6	-4.6	33.7	19.7	26.5
mixed	32.1	47.1	35.9	5.6	1.3	5.7	8.8	6.4	15.0
all types (excluding horticulture)	29.3	39.3	30.7	13.4	8.9	6.6	8.4	10.1	12.5
In real terms (at 2001/02 prices)									
United Kingdom									
dairy	40.4	47.9	37.8	23.3	13.6	9.9	12.6	23.2	17.0
cattle and sheep (LFA) (b)	9.5	14.2	13.8	7.2	3.4	2.0	3.9	4.8	9.5
cattle and sheep (lowland)	9.4	9.9	8.0	0.7	-0.3	-	-	0.4	7.0
cereals	40.6	62.1	54.0	17.9	8.8	13.8	6.9	3.3	7.0
general cropping	89.5	101.2	51.2	21.7	36.8	8.2	19.1	15.7	13.0
pigs and poultry	32.0	65.9	58.3	19.3	-18.7	-4.8	34.2	19.7	26.0
mixed	38.5	54.7	40.7	6.1	1.4	5.9	8.9	6.4	15.0
all types (excluding horticulture)	35.2	45.6	34.7	14.7	9.4	6.9	8.6	10.1	12.5

source: Defra website, www.defra.gov.uk/esg

(a) Excluding farms subjected to compulsory Foot and Mouth Disease cull.

(b) Less Favoured Areas.

London: TSO
April 2003

Agriculture in the United Kingdom 2002

Produced by:

...onment, Food and Rural Affairs

...ronment and Rural ...Affairs Department

...riculture and Rural ...(Northern Ireland)

...es Agriculture and ...Affairs Department

LONDON: TSO

Published by TSO (The Stationery Office) and available from:

Online
www.tso.co.uk/bookshop

Mail, Telephone, Fax and E-mail
TSO
PO Box 29, Norwich, NR3 1GN

Telephone orders/General enquiries: 0870 600 5522
Fax orders: 0870 600 5533
E-mail: book.orders@tso.co.uk
Textphone 0870 240 3701

TSO Shops
123 Kingsway, London, WC2B 6PQ
020 7242 6393 Fax 020 7242 6394
68-69 Bull Street, Birmingham B4 6AD
0121 236 9696 Fax 0121 236 9699
9-21 Princess Street, Manchester M60 8AS
0161 834 7201 Fax 0161 833 0634
16 Arthur Street, Belfast BT1 4GD
028 9023 8451 Fax 028 9023 5401
18-19 High Street, Cardiff CF10 1PT
029 2039 5548 Fax 029 2038 4347
71 Lothian Road, Edinburgh EH3 9AZ
0870 606 5566 Fax 0870 606 5588

TSO Accredited Agents
(see Yellow Pages)

and through good booksellers

First published 2003

ISBN 0 11 243070 8

The paper on which this publication is printed uses pulp from managed forests only and is Total Chlorine Free (TCF)

Printed in the United Kingdom for The Stationery Office
Id 127236 3/03 828897 19585

2002

Contents

Statistical tables and charts

List of tables

2002

List of charts

Preface

Legal basis **1** Agriculture in the United Kingdom 2002 fulfils the requirement under the Agriculture Act 1993 that Ministers publish an annual report on such matters relating to price support for agricultural produce as they consider relevant. The government will draw on this information when considering policy issues, including proposals by the European Commission in respect of the Common Agricultural Policy and the provision of agricultural support in 2002/03.

Changes to the report **2** Some of the figures now given for past years may differ from those published in preceding issues. This is because of the use of later information, changes in the scope and nature of the available data and improvements in statistical methods. Chapter 10 has been expanded in line with the greater emphasis given to environmental aspects of agriculture.

Statistical notices **3** Most of the data are on a calendar year basis. The figures for 2002 are provisional; they reflect the position at January 2003 when information for 2002 was still incomplete and an element of forecasting was required.

4 The following points apply throughout:

(a) All figures relate to the United Kingdom, unless otherwise stated.

(b) In the tables

- means 'nil' or 'negligible'.

. . means 'not available' or 'not applicable'.

(c) The figures for imports and exports include those from intervention stocks and the figures for exports include re-exports. Imports are based on country of consignment. Exports are based on country of reported final destination. The source of overseas trade statistics is HM Customs and Excise.

(d) Where statistics are shown for the European Union as a whole, they represent the present 15 Member States in all years. For example, exports of food, feed and drink to the EU in 1991 to 1993 includes exports to all 15 member states during that period.

5 This publication and other Defra statistics can be found on the internet at www.defra.gov.uk/esg.

Chapter **1** Key events in 2002

Foot and Mouth Disease

1 After the devastating outbreak of Foot and Mouth Disease in 2001 all counties became officially FMD-free on 14 January 2002. On 22 January 2002 the UK regained its status as an FMD-free country for the purposes of international trade in animals and animal products following a decision by the Office International des Epizooties (OIE) in Paris. There were a number of investigations into suspect cases in 2002; all proved negative for Foot and Mouth Disease.

2 In August 2001 the government announced three independent inquiries to report to the Prime Minister and Secretary of State for Environment, Food and Rural Affairs: (a) the lessons to be learned and the way any future outbreaks should be handled; (b) a scientific review by the Royal Society of questions relating to transmission, prevention and control of epidemic outbreaks of infectious disease in livestock; and (c) a policy commission, to cover England only, on the future of farming and food. All three inquiries reported in 2002.

3 The Policy Commission on the Future of Farming and Food was established in August 2001 with Sir Donald Curry as its Chairman. It was given five months to complete its remit to advise the government on how to create a sustainable, competitive and diverse farming and food sector. The Commission's report "Farming and Food: A Sustainable Future" was published on 29 January 2002. On 12 December 2002 the Prime Minister and Secretary of State for Environment, Food and Rural Affairs launched the government strategy for farming and food in England, building on the work of the Policy Commission's report, with the publication of "The Strategy for Sustainable Farming and Food - Facing the Future". Two further documents were published on the same date - "Response to the Report of the Policy Commission on the Future of Farming and Food by HM Government" and "Farming and Food's Contribution to Sustainable Development - Economic and Statistical Analysis".

4 The Royal Society inquiry, chaired by Professor Sir Brian Follett, published its report on 16 July. Dr Iain Anderson conducted the enquiry into the government's handling of the outbreak and published his report "Foot and Mouth Disease: Lessons to be Learned Inquiry Report" on 22 July. In November 2002 the government's "Response to the Reports of the Foot and Mouth Disease Inquiries" was presented to Parliament by the Secretary of State for Environment, Food and Rural Affairs.

5 The government's response sets out a wide range of actions, commitments and decisions including the government's Strategy for Sustainable Farming and Food in England whose publication has been noted above. Defra's contingency plan, which provides a framework for an emergency response to a Foot and Mouth Disease outbreak, was comprehensively reviewed as a result of the recommendations made in these reports.

6 During 2002 animal movements and gatherings continued to be subject to controls, based on veterinary and scientific advice, to protect the livestock industry from disease spread following any fresh incursion of Foot and Mouth Disease. The centrepiece of these controls was the 20 day standstill..

Copies of these regulations and the Inquiry reports are available on Defra's website at www.defra.gov.uk/footandmouth.

Weather report 7 After a dry, cold December the remainder of the winter of 2001/2002 was characterised by mild, damp weather. Autumn-sown crops continued to benefit from the favourable planting conditions of the autumn and emerged from the winter in good condition. An exceedingly wet February finally gave way to warm and sunny weather in the second half of March allowing stock to be turned out in many areas and spring land work to commence. It was the sunniest April over England and Wales since 1990, although low night temperatures kept plant growth in check. The dry weather coincided with lambing in many areas and there were reports of the easiest lambing for several years. Lambing percentages were also much improved compared to the previous year with an estimate of 108% compared to 99% for 2001.

8 By May many farmers were crying out for rain which duly arrived in the latter half of the month. At this stage conditions were ideal for arable crops and a bumper harvest was predicted. However, in western areas, such as Northern Ireland, above average rainfall was hindering farming operations. The lack of sunshine across the UK in June and July was considered responsible for poor grain fill, and although yields in England and Wales were substantially better than in 2001, the bumper harvest did not materialise. The harvest was fraught with difficulties in some areas, particularly in the east of England where thunderstorms swept across the region. The quality of late harvested wheat crops was impaired resulting in a premium for high Hagberg milling wheats combined before the rain.

9 The predominance of wet weather throughout the summer meant that grass was plentiful for livestock producers, although hay and silage making were often difficult especially in Northern Ireland, where rainfall in each of the months April to July was more than 50 per cent above normal. In general terms, fodder quality is probably poorer than last year. In Northern Ireland, the adverse weather not only led to poor quality fodder, but stock were also housed early and there was increased use of concentrate feedstuffs.

10 September was a dry month across virtually the whole of the UK providing excellent sowing conditions and allowing the potato harvest to progress unhampered. With the exception of Northern Ireland, the dry start to the autumn also enabled the grazing season to be extended with reduced supplementary feeding costs. However, it was followed by a very wet October and November in all regions except northern Scotland. Some arable crops drilled early were slow to germinate due to lack of moisture, but the majority went into the winter in good condition. Grass weeds, however, could be a problem as the wet weather made spraying difficult. The year ended very wet and mild with some flooding in southern and western areas. Around 1.6 million tonnes of sugar beet were still to be lifted at the end of the year,

representing 19% of the crop.

Performance indicators **11** Total Income From Farming (TIFF) rose in real terms by 14 per cent to £2.4 billion in 2002 compared with 2001, but was still 62 per cent below its peak in 1995. Gross Value Added for the industry (which represents agriculture's contribution to national GDP) rose by 12 per cent in volume and 3.9 per cent in value (current prices). Paid labour fell by 4.6 per cent in 2002 which was greater than the fall in 2001, but less than the 12 per cent fall in 2000. Total factor productivity rose by 7.4 per cent. Cash flow from farming fell 38 per cent in real terms, or 1.5 billion to £2.5 billion. This was a result of the high cash flow of 2001 when farmers were compensated for destroyed livestock due to Foot and Mouth Disease.

Exchange rates 1990-2002

£ per euro

12 The relatively high level of sterling has been the dominant factor behind the steep decline in incomes since the mid 1990s. Farming is particularly exposed to exchange rate movements because the value of most outputs is highly sensitive to shifts in the pound/euro rate, whilst prices of inputs tend to be less sensitive. The result was that the decline in the pound after the UK left the Exchange Rate Mechanism (ERM) in 1992 lead to a boom in farming's profitability. This was reversed as the pound grew stronger in the latter half of the 1990s. The pound/euro exchange rate in 2002 was 0.63 pounds per euro, maintaining the steady increase from a low of 0.61 pounds per euro in 2000.

13 Eurostat and agriculture departments are developing indicators to identify, quantify and evaluate the effects of agriculture on, and progress towards, sustainability. Standards need to be established, but some data are already available. Chapter 10 gives further details.

Subsidies **14** Direct subsidies, less levies, paid to the industry rose slightly to £2.6 billion. Spending in the UK under the CAP is forecast to increase from £3.1 billion in 2001/2002 to £3.4 billion in 2002/03.

15 Arable Area Payments totalled £981 million in 2002, which was £11 million more than in 2001. There was a 22 per cent increase in the area of wheat but a 24 per cent decrease in the area of set-aside.

16 Subsidies and other income payments to the livestock sector rose by 8.2 per cent to £1.2 billion. Payments to beef producers rose, as did payments under the Sheep Annual Premium Scheme partly due to a new method for fixing subsidy rates.

17 The rate of modulation, introduced in 2001 at a flat rate of 2.5 per cent, was increased to 3.0 per cent in the 2002 scheme year. On an accruals basis modulation is estimated to reduce arable and livestock subsidies by around £60 million in 2002. Payments under agri-environment schemes were £47 million higher than in 2001.

European Union Developments **18** On 10 July 2002 the European Commission published a discussion document containing its proposals for major changes to the Common Agricultural Policy (CAP) - the so-called Mid-term Review (MTR). The Commission proposals include some market support regime reforms: a removal of the link between production and support ('decoupling'), and a reinforcing of rural development funding to boost quality production, environmental protection, food safety, and animal welfare. A revised CAP will contribute towards delivering: prosperous rural areas; a better deal for the environment; safe food; high animal welfare standards; a better deal for farmers; better value for money, and help for developing countries through resultant liberalised trade. The European Commission published its draft legislative texts on 22 January 2003.

19   The European Council announced at its summit held in Copenhagen in December 2002 that accession negotiations had been successfully concluded with the following 10 candidate countries: Cyprus, the Czech Republic, Estonia, Hungary, Latvia, Lithuania, Malta, Poland, the Slovak Republic and Slovenia. These countries will join the EU on 1 May 2004 bringing the total number of Member States to 25.

Chapter **2** Farming income and agriculture in the economy

Long Term Trends in
Farming Income
(Chart 2.1)

1 Although having risen in 2001 and 2002, Total Income from Farming (TIFF) is still in real terms 62 per cent below its peak in 1995 (after more than doubling between 1990 and 1995). The long term trend in income has been downwards, although incomes rose and fell dramatically in the nineties due to changes in exchange rates, world commodity prices and the impact of BSE.

Chart 2.1 UK income trends in real terms at 2002 prices

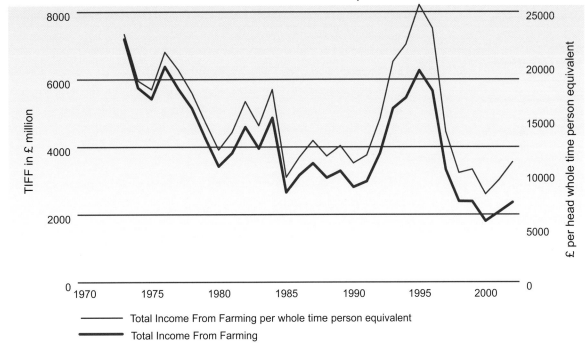

Total Income From Farming per whole time person equivalent
Total Income From Farming

Summary Measures
including Total
Income from Farming
(Table 2.1)

2 Total Income from Farming in the UK in 2002 is estimated to be £2.4 billion which is 15 per cent (14 per cent in real terms) higher than its 2001 level. TIFF is income generated by production within the agriculture industry, including subsidies. It represents business profits plus remuneration for work done by owners and other unpaid workers. TIFF per whole-time person equivalent rose by 19 per cent (18 per cent in real terms) to £11,107. Average subsidies per whole-time person equivalent of entrepreneurial labour were higher at £14,317 in real terms, a 12 per cent increase on 2001. However, the distribution of subsidies is far from equal.

3 The overall increase in income for 2002 masks variation across the sectors and individual countries. The value of output (including subsidies directly related to products) was slightly higher, up by £168 million or 1.1 per cent. The volume was 4.8 per cent higher but prices received were 3.6 per cent lower.

4 There were notable increases in the value of output for cereals (8.4 per cent) and livestock (8.3 per cent). For cereals, an increase in wheat (22 per cent) more than offset a decrease in barley (14 per cent) as wheat production returned to more normal levels following the impact of the wet weather on the 2001 harvest. For livestock, poultry decreased by 8.0 per cent whilst cattle and sheep increased by 14 and 34 per cent respectively, as production recovered after Foot and Mouth Disease and sheep prices increased by 21 per cent.

5   There were notable decreases in the value of output for potatoes (27 per cent) and milk (12 per cent). Milk fell by £333 million as prices received by farmers dropped by 11 per cent.

6   Cash flow from farming fell 38 per cent in real terms, or £1.5 billion to £2.5 billion. This is a result of the high cash flow of 2001 when farmers were compensated for destroyed livestock due to Foot and Mouth Disease. Cash flow reflects sales rather than production, and expenditure on gross fixed capital formation rather than depreciation of capital assets. It includes capital transfers paid to the industry in exchange for assets.

7   Total factor productivity increased by 7.4 per cent in 2002; output increased and inputs (including labour) declined slightly. The reason for the large productivity gains compared to last year is that productivity was unusually low in 2001 when Foot and Mouth Disease and wet weather led to a large fall.

Agriculture in the national economy
(Table 2.2)

8   Gross Value Added for the industry, which represents its contribution to national GDP, increased by 3.9 per cent, driven by an increase in output and a decrease in intermediate consumption.

9   The agricultural industry has accounted for around 0.8 per cent of the total economy since 2000, measured in terms of Gross Value Added. Since 1973, when the share was almost 3 per cent, the overall trend has been downwards, although there have been brief recoveries when prices for agricultural commodities improved.

10   The industry's share of the total workforce has fallen nearly every year and is now at 1.9 per cent. The volume of paid labour fell by 4.6 per cent in 2002 and unpaid labour by slightly less, 3.4 per cent. Since the early 1980s there has been a shift in the composition of the labour force with an increase in part-time workers - rising from 25 per cent to about 50 per cent of the total.

Food in the national economy
(Table 2.2 and chart 2.2)

Food index and RPI
1987 = 100

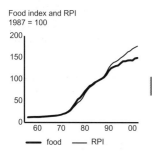

11   Imports of food, feed and drink cost £18.9 billion in 2002, more than twice the value of exports which were worth £9.0 billion. In 2001 the volume of imports increased significantly, while exports decreased due to the effects of Foot and Mouth Disease on trade, especially meat and animal feed. The volume of trade in 2002 hardly altered as trade was slow to recover. Food prices rose marginally in 2002, up 0.7 per cent. All prices, as measured by the retail price index, rose by 1.6 per cent.

12   Consumers' expenditure on food and alcoholic drinks increased in 2002 by 5.5 per cent continuing recent trends. In real terms (constant 1995 prices), expenditure increased by 2.4 per cent. Expenditure on food eaten out increased by more than that on household consumption or alcoholic drinks. Expenditure on food and drink remained at roughly the same proportion of total household final consumption expenditure.

13　Self-sufficiency in food in 2002 was at its lowest level since the current series began in 1988. The UK was 62 per cent self-sufficient in all food and 75 per cent in indigenous food. The ban on UK meat exports imposed as a result of the Foot and Mouth Disease outbreak in 2001 was fully lifted in February 2002. Despite this, exports of meat have not recovered and imports have continued to rise slightly. There has also been a small increase in imports of indigenous fruit and vegetables. Self-sufficiency is calculated as the value of raw food for human consumption divided by the value of production of raw food.

Chart 2.2 The UK food chain

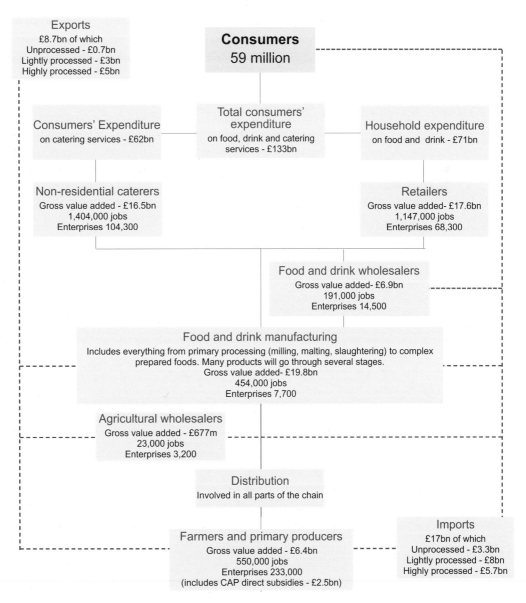

Exports
£8.7bn of which
Unprocessed - £0.7bn
Lightly processed - £3bn
Highly processed - £5bn

Consumers
59 million

Total consumers'
expenditure
on food, drink and catering
services - £133bn

Consumers' Expenditure
on catering services - £62bn

Household expenditure
on food and drink - £71bn

Non-residential caterers
Gross value added - £16.5bn
1,404,000 jobs
Enterprises 104,300

Retailers
Gross value added- £17.6bn
1,147,000 jobs
Enterprises 68,300

Food and drink wholesalers
Gross value added- £6.9bn
191,000 jobs
Enterprises 14,500

Food and drink manufacturing
Includes everything from primary processing (milling, malting, slaughtering) to complex prepared foods. Many products will go through several stages.
Gross value added- £19.8bn
454,000 jobs
Enterprises 7,700

Agricultural wholesalers
Gross value added - £677m
23,000 jobs
Enterprises 3,200

Distribution
Involved in all parts of the chain

Farmers and primary producers
Gross value added - £6.4bn
550,000 jobs
Enterprises 233,000
(includes CAP direct subsidies - £2.5bn)

Imports
£17bn of which
Unprocessed - £3.3bn
Lightly processed - £8bn
Highly processed - £5.7bn

(a) Employment data relates to employment at June 2002.

(b) Data on agricultural merchants provided by United Kingdom Agricultural Supply Trade Association (UKASTA.)

14　Chart 2.2 shows agriculture's position as a primary producer in the food chain. Whilst agriculture's share of the UK economy, measured in terms of Gross Value Added at basic prices, was only 0.8 per cent in 2001, the agri-food sector as a whole accounted for broadly 8 per cent. Consumers' expenditure on food, drink and catering was £133 billion in 2001. The UK food supply chain as a whole had £125 billion at its disposal, coming from consumers' expenditure, plus exports less imports of agricultural commodities, and processed food and drink products (assuming that imports and exports directly to and from consumers are negligible). Total employment in the food chain measured in June 2002 amounted to nearly 3.8 million people, of which over half a million were in agriculture.

Prospects for farming incomes
(Chart 2.3)

15   The future business prospects for farming will reflect the interaction of the key drivers (both long-term and short-term) which have shaped the present position. Chart 2.3 shows some stylised projections of underlying trends; it should be emphasised that these types of projection have very broad margins of uncertainty and also that agriculture is an industry where specific events - a disease outbreak or poor weather - can shift incomes from the underlying trend in individual years.

Chart 2.3 Projections of Total Income from Farming up to 2007

Real terms at 2002 prices per whole time person equivalent

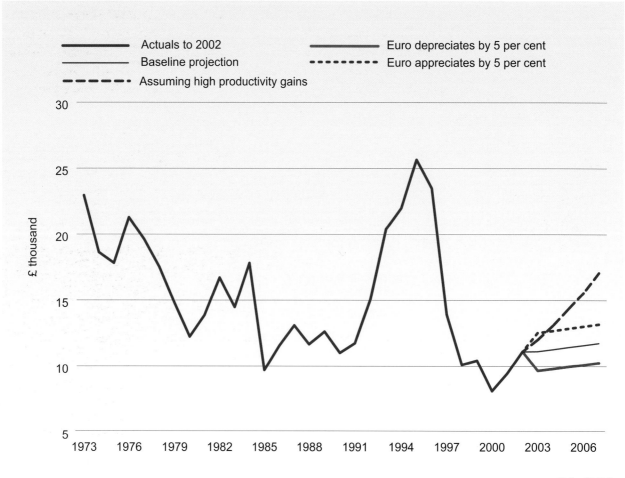

source: Defra Statistics

16   The projections indicate that the modest extent of expected recovery in world commodity markets over the next five years is likely to provide for only a marginal increase in the average level of income per farmer; future forecasts of world commodity prices are, however, quite uncertain.

Exchange rates 1990-2002

£ per euro

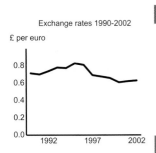

17 A second key driver is the pound/euro exchange rate, and the projections show the potential importance of this. Most private sector macroeconomic forecasters expect the euro to rise against the pound but there is considerable uncertainty on how much of a shift is likely and on what timescale. Many of the forecasters expect a shift of up to 5% on 2002 levels, and the chart shows that this would leave incomes at a relatively depressed level.

18 The other key driver is productivity. UK productivity growth has generally been slower compared with many other EU countries. Chart 2.3 shows what might happen if this trend could be reversed by sustaining the exceptionally high rates of productivity growth which were achieved in the late 1990s.

Geographic comparisons (Tables 2.3, 2.4, 2.5, 2.6 and chart 2.4)

19 Table 2.3 shows how the UK agricultural industry divides between England, Northern Ireland, Scotland and Wales. Agriculture's share of total economy Gross Value Added is generally declining. Agriculture's share of regional employment is highest in Northern Ireland at about 1 in 12 whereas in England it is less than 1 in 60.

20 Chart 2.4 shows estimated changes in income from agricultural activity across the Member States of the European Union, as measured by Eurostat's indicator A. It is based on Net Value Added at factor cost (deflated by the GDP price index), which is a measure of agricultural income, per annual work unit (full-time worker equivalent). This income measure is estimated to have declined by 3.0 per cent in

Chart 2.4 Changes in income across the European Union

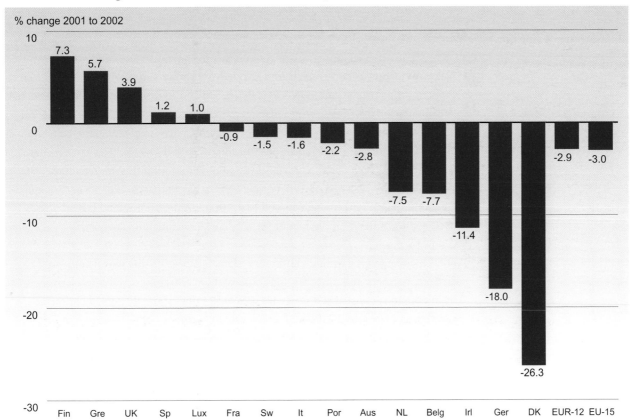

The change in income from agricultural activity as measured by Eurostat, Indicator A, which is based on net value added per full-time worker equivalent.

Source: Eurostat - Statistics : Statistics in focus, December 2002

2002 in the European Union as a whole, and declined in ten of the fifteen Member States. The largest falls were recorded in Denmark (-26%), Germany (-18%) and Ireland (-11%). In five countries incomes were higher in 2002 than in 2001 with the largest increases in Finland (7.3%), Greece (5.7%) and the UK (3.9%).

21   Table 2.5 shows the relative importance of agriculture in the 15 Member States in 2000. The share of agriculture in national Gross Value Added is lowest in the UK (0.4%), followed by Finland and Sweden (both 0.5%). Agriculture's share in national Gross Value Added is highest with 4.7 per cent in Greece, followed by Spain with 3.2 per cent. For the European Union as a whole (EU-15), agriculture accounts for 4.0 per cent of employment. However, agriculture's importance in employment varies greatly from one Member State to another. In Greece, almost 17 per cent of national employment is in agriculture. The UK has the lowest rate with 1.4 per cent.

Table 2.6 compares Eurostat's income indicators in the UK and in the European Union as a whole. While income per full-time worker equivalent (indicator A) has increased in EU-15 since 1995, it has declined by 40 per cent in the UK over the same period. Income indicator C, which shows total entrepreneurial income for the agricultural industry, has declined since 1995 both in EU-15 and in the UK. The fall in the UK was much larger (-67% as opposed to -12% in the EU as a whole).

Net farm incomes by farm type
(Table 2.7)

22   Information on incomes, assets and liabilities of full time businesses in the UK is provided by the annual Farm Business Surveys, conducted by universities and agricultural colleges in England and Wales, the Department of Agriculture and Rural Development in Northern Ireland, and the Farm Accounts Scheme in Scotland carried out by the Scottish Agricultural College.

23   Net farm income is constructed so that the profitability and performance of different types of farms can be compared. It is defined as the return to the principal farmer and spouse for their manual and managerial labour and on the tenant-type capital of the business. Tenant-type assets, which for this purpose are all assumed to be owned by the occupier, include crops, machinery and livestock. Net farm income treats all farms on a consistent basis by assuming that all farms are tenanted. Thus the profitability of farms of different tenure can be compared. For owner-occupied land an imputed rent is included as a cost. In addition, an imputed labour cost is deducted for unpaid family labour (other than the farmer and spouse).

24   Total Income from Farming (TIFF) represents business profits plus income to farmers, partners and directors and those with an entrepreneurial interest in the business and is constructed in accordance with internationally agreed national accounting principles. TIFF and its underlying estimates of outputs and inputs feed into the national accounts and ultimately the national estimate for GDP.

25.   As can be seen from their respective definitions, net farm income is a narrower income measure than TIFF. As a consequence the annual percentage change in net farm income is more volatile, especially at relatively low levels of income.

26   Movements in net farm income over the last decade for each UK region and for the

2002

TIFF - Aggregate Measure	NET FARM INCOME - Farm Level Measure
Gross output at basic prices	Receipts from sales of output plus subsidies
plus	*plus*
Other subsidies less taxes	Crop and livestock valuation change
less	*less*
Total intermediate consumption, rent, paid labour	Expenditure (costs, overheads, fuel, repairs, rent, paid labour)
Total consumption of fixed capital (depreciation)	Depreciation of tenant capital
Interest	Imputed value of unpaid labour
	Imputed rent for owner occupiers
equals	*equals*
Total Income from Farming	Net farm income

major farm types (excluding horticulture) are shown in Table 2.7. Net farm income figures are for an accounting period that runs from March to February on average, cover full-time farms only and exclude horticulture. Also, note that whereas the net farm income figures presented in table 2.7 exclude those farms subjected to the compulsory cull of animals during the Foot and Mouth Disease epidemic, TIFF statistics include such farms.

27 Average net farm income in the UK increased by 19% between 2000/01 and 2001/02. The majority of this increase was attributable to a significant rise in the net farm income of dairy farms (87%). With the exception of cattle and sheep (least favoured area and lowland) all other farm types faced a fall in net farm income.

28 Average UK net farm income peaked in 1995/96 at £39,200 and steadily fell to a low point of £6,600 in 1999/00. Since this date, average net farm income gradually rose to £10,100 in 2001/02.

29 Provisional estimates of net farm income for 2002/03 are shown in Table 2.7. These are based on data from 2001/02 accounts projected forward to 2002/03 on the basis of information on prices in 2002/03, subsidy payments, animal populations and marketings, and crop areas and yields. The estimates should be regarded only as broad indicators of the overall effects on income of expected changes in output values and input costs. Forecasts exclude those farms subjected to the compulsory cull of livestock during the Foot and Mouth Disease crisis.

30 Average net farm income in 2002/03 is forecast to increase by 30%. This is mainly due to a marked increase in incomes on cattle and sheep farms both in the less favoured areas (LFA) and lowland. Strong market prices for finished lambs and store sheep and cattle and increased headage payments, particularly Sheep Annual Premium, are the main contributory factors. Cereal net farm incomes are expected to increase by 115% as yields improve from the poor harvest of 2001 and cropping area increases. Incomes on dairy and general cropping farms are expected to

decline. This reflects a fall in milk prices and, on general cropping farms, lower potato prices offsetting any improvement in yield or increase in cereal output. Pig and poultry farms are expected to see an increase of 36% in net farm incomes. This increase is mainly driven by higher egg prices and lower feed costs, particularly cereals.

Table 2.1 Summary measures from the aggregate agricultural account

Inquiries: Christine Jeannette on 01904 455080   email: christine.jeannette@defra.gsi.gov.uk

Calendar years

Year	Net value added at factor cost	Income from farming				Cash flow from farming
		Total income from farming	Compensation of employees	Income from agriculture of total labour input	Total income from farming per AWU of entrepreneurial labour (a)	
£ million		A	B	A + B	(£)	
1991	5 039	2 263	1 779	4 042	8 901	2 832
1992	5 669	2 996	1 784	4 780	11 839	3 196
1993	6 597	4 108	1 787	5 894	16 282	4 145
1994	7 011	4 465	1 827	6 293	17 992	4 422
1995	7 898	5 299	1 836	7 136	21 710	5 125
1996	7 569	4 906	1 881	6 787	20 353	4 932
1997	5 783	2 977	1 930	4 906	12 440	3 222
1998	5 117	2 210	1 977	4 187	9 351	2 965
1999	5 103	2 240	2 030	4 270	9 791	3 083
2000	4 492	1 742	1 903	3 646	7 848	2 820
2001	4 752	2 041	1 909	3 950	9 298	3 908
2002 (provisional)	4 990	2 356	1 907	4 263	11 107	2 472
In real terms, 2002 prices, £ million		A	B	A + B	(£)	
1991	6 648	2 985	2 347	5 332	11 743	3 736
1992	7 210	3 810	2 268	6 079	15 057	4 065
1993	8 261	5 144	2 237	7 381	20 388	5 190
1994	8 567	5 456	2 233	7 689	21 986	5 404
1995	9 333	6 262	2 170	8 432	25 654	6 056
1996	8 730	5 658	2 169	7 828	23 476	5 688
1997	6 468	3 329	2 158	5 487	13 913	3 603
1998	5 534	2 390	2 138	4 527	10 113	3 206
1999	5 434	2 385	2 162	4 547	10 425	3 283
2000	4 647	1 803	1 969	3 772	8 120	2 918
2001	4 829	2 074	1 940	4 014	9 447	3 971
2002 (provisional)	4 990	2 356	1 907	4 263	11 107	2 472

source: Defra website, www.defra.gov.uk/esg

a)   An annual work unit (AWU) represents the equivalent of an average full-time worker engaged in agriculture.

Table 2.2 Agriculture and food in the national economy

Inquiries: Christine Jeannette on 01904 455080   email: christine.jeannette@defra.gsi.gov.uk   Calendar years

	Average of 1991-1993	1998	1999	2000	2001	2002 (provisional)
Agriculture's contribution to total economy Gross Value Added (a)						
at current prices (£ million)	8 112	7 562	7 288	6 749	6 850	7 117
volume index (1995=100)	104.4	103.0	107.1	106.8	95.3	106.2
% of total economy Gross Value Added (current prices)	1.5	1.0	0.9	0.8	0.8	0.8
Workforce in agriculture ('000 persons) (b) (c)	637	608	586	557	568	550
% of total workforce in employment	2.4	2.2	2.1	1.9	1.9	1.9
Gross fixed capital formation (GFCF) in agriculture						
total GFCF at current prices (£ million)	2 135	2 007	1 644	1 591	2 024	2 318
% of national GFCF (current prices)	2.1	1.4	1.1	1.0	1.3	1.6
volume indices (1995=100):						
buildings and works, plant and machinery, vehicles	79.1	65.8	56.9	53.8	62.0	68.2
livestock	96.9	107.9	103.9	88.0	102.4	101.9
Imports of food, feed and drink (£ million) (d) (e)	13 231	17 198	17 385	17 018	18 335	18 905
imports from the EU:	8 659	10 979	11 164	10 910	11 649	12 012
of which: food, feed and non alcoholic drinks	7 409	9 198	9 341	9 327	10 054	10 321
alcoholic drinks	1 250	1 781	1 823	1 584	1 595	1 691
imports from the rest of the world:	4 572	6 220	6 221	6 107	6 686	6 893
of which: food, feed and non alcoholic drinks	4 346	5 565	5 464	5 267	5 691	5 789
alcoholic drinks	225	655	757	841	996	1 104
volume index (1995=100) (f)	91.7	119.4	128.6	128.0	138.2	137.7
% of total UK imports	10.4	9.0	8.8	7.6	8.0	8.4
Exports of food, feed and drink (£ million) (d) (e)	7 529	9 246	8 948	8 737	8 558	8 950
exports to the EU:	4 865	5 865	5 709	5 348	5 193	5 537
of which: food, feed and non alcoholic drinks	3 903	4 738	4 505	4 152	3 972	4 229
alcoholic drinks	962	1 128	1 204	1 196	1 222	1 307
exports to the rest of the world:	2 664	3 381	3 239	3 389	3 365	3 414
of which: food, feed and non alcoholic drinks	1 252	1 745	1 582	1 645	1 499	1 434
alcoholic drinks	1 411	1 636	1 656	1 744	1 867	1 980
volume index (1995=100) (f)	81.2	101.2	102.5	101.9	98.8	99.3
% of total UK exports	6.8	5.6	5.4	4.7	4.5	4.8
UK self-sufficiency in food as a % of:						
all food	74.4	67.7	67.8	67.0	62.5	62.2
indigenous type food	85.8	82.0	81.7	80.4	74.8	74.9
Household final consumption expenditure on						
food and alcoholic drinks at current prices (£ million)(g)	..	116 213	121 812	126 840	133 669	140 978
of which: household food	45 810	55 192	56 625	57 719	60 277	62 844
food eaten out	..	29 242	31 502	34 615	36 072	38 831
alcoholic drinks	24 061	31 779	33 685	34 506	37 320	39 302
at constant 1995 prices (£ million)	..	107 796	110 622	113 426	116 080	118 820
of which: household food	48 427	52 983	54 102	55 610	56 150	57 309
food eaten out	..	26 094	27 197	28 282	28 853	30 109
alcoholic drinks	26 804	28 719	29 323	29 534	31 077	31 402
% of total household final consumption expenditure	..	21.7	21.4	21.0	21.2	21.2
of which: household food	12.1	10.3	9.9	9.6	9.6	9.5
food eaten out	..	5.5	5.5	5.7	5.7	5.8
alcoholic drinks	6.3	5.9	5.9	5.7	5.9	5.9
Retail price indices (1995=100)						
food	93.6	104.7	105.0	104.7	108.2	108.9
alcoholic drinks	89.6	109.4	112.2	113.9	116.3	118.8
all items	92.3	109.3	111.0	114.2	116.3	118.2

source: Defra website, www.defra.gov.uk/esg

Table 2.2 *cont*

(a) In order to estimate the total Gross Value Added (GVA) at basic prices for the entire economy, the fourth quarter has been estimated using the trend of the previous three quarters. Data not available from the Office for National Statistics (ONS) for individual countries.

(b) This series includes spouses of farmers, partners and directors These were excluded prior to 2000 edition because consistent data were not available for years before 1998.

(c) From 1998 onwards figures are on a different basis to previous years. From 2001, figures include the effect of the register improvement in England and are NOT directly comparable with

earlier years. See also table 3.5.

(d) This aggregate covers SITC divisions 01-09, 11, 22 and section 4.

(e) The figures for 1993 onwards are based on INTRASTAT data and include estimates of non-response and of traders below the threshold for which detailed trade data are not collected.

(f) Data provided by Office for National Statistics (ONS).

(g) 'Household final consumption expenditure' replaced 'Consumer's expenditure' in 1998 when National Accounts adopted the European System of Accounts.

Table 2.3 Summary measures by country in 2002

Inquiries: Christine Jeannette on 01904 455080   email: christine.jeannette@defra.gsi.gov.uk

	Gross output (a)	Intermediate consumption	Gross value added at basic prices	Total Income from Farming	Agriculture's share of total regional Gross Value Added at basic prices (b)	Agriculture's share of total regional employment (c)(d)
	£ million	£ million	£ million	£ million	%	%
United Kingdom	15 508	8 391	7 117	2 356	0.8	1.9
England	11 493	5 997	5 496	1 845	. .	1.5
Wales	1 012	631	381	116	. .	4.5
Scotland	1 861	1 070	791	268	. .	2.7
Northern Ireland	1 142	694	448	127	. .	7.2

source:Defra website, www.defra.gov.uk/esg

(a) Imported livestock, including purchases of store cattle and sheep, are included as negative output.

(b).In order to estimate the total Gross Value Added (GVA) at basic prices for the entire economy, the fourth quarter has been estimated using the trend of the previous three quarters. Data not available from the Office for National Statistics (ONS) for individual countries.

(c) The total workforce in employment consists of employees in employment, the self-employed and work related government training schemes. For Northern Ireland, agriculture's percentage share is higher than that published by the Northern Ireland

Department of Enterprise, Trade and Investment, which excludes part-time owners, partners and directors and spouses of farmers from persons engaged in agriculture.

(d) The agriculture industry includes a high proportion of part-time workers. A comparison on the basis of full-time equivalents would show lower percentages.

Table 2.4 Summary measures by region in 2000

Inquiries: Christine Jeannette on 01904 455080   email: christine.jeannette@defra.gsi.gov.uk

	Gross output (a)	Intermediate consumption	Gross value added at basic prices	Total Income from Farming	Agriculture's share of total regional Gross Value Added at basic prices	Agriculture's share of total regional employment (b)(c)
	£ million	£ million	£ million	£ million	%	%
United Kingdom	15 022	8 487	6 535	1 513	0.8	2.0
England	11 045	6 185	4 860	1 106	..	1.6
Wales	1 004	642	362	46	..	4.7
Scotland	1 878	1 030	848	245	..	3.0
Northern Ireland	1 095	630	465	116	..	7.9
English Regions						
North East	373	232	141	11	..	1.1
North West	1 049	619	430	51	..	1.3
Yorkshire and Humberside	1 450	763	687	264	..	1.7
East Midlands	1 544	869	675	173	..	2.3
West Midlands	1 272	708	564	142	..	1.8
East of England	2 042	1 064	979	336	..	2.1
South East and London	1 356	725	631	76	..	0.7
South West	1 959	1 206	753	55	..	3.4

source:Defra website, www.defra.gov.uk/esg

(a) Imported livestock, including purchases of store cattle and sheep, are included as negative output.

(b) The total workforce in employment consists of employees in employment, the self-employed and work-related government training schemes. For Northern Ireland, agriculture's percentage share is higher than that published by the Northern Ireland

Department of Enterprise, Trade and Investment, which excludes from persons engaged in agriculture part-time owners, partners and directors and spouses of farmers .

(c) The agriculture industry includes a high proportion of part-time workers. A comparison on the basis of full-time equivalents would show lower percentages.

Table 2.5 Comparison of agriculture in EU countries 2000

Inquiries: Christine Jeannette on 01904 455080   email: christine.jeannette@defra.gsi.gov.uk

	Belg	DK	Ger	Gre	Sp	Fra	Irl	It	Lux	NL	Aus	Por	Fin	Sw	UK	EUR-12	EU-15
Country comparison of agriculture at current prices and current exchange rates, € million (€ = £0.6095)																	
Total crop output	3 024	3 223	21 521	7 961	20 683	35 899	1 163	26 604	85	9 634	2 446	3 125	1 718	2 431	9 081	133 862	148 597
Total animal output	3 882	4 808	19 892	2 701	12 144	23 829	4 374	13 505	159	8 117	2 470	2 428	1 930	2 423	13 416	95 432	116 079
Gross output	6 983	8 344	42 913	11 112	34 070	63 752	5 812	41 760	258	19 288	5 465	5 558	3 884	5 127	24 435	240 855	278 761
Gross value added	2 685	3 546	17 598	8 216	22 623	31 719	2 702	28 341	130	8 763	2 444	2 713	1 269	1 675	10 511	129 202	144 934
Entrepreneurial income	1 298	1 029	4 645	6 622	16 090	14 985	1 860	14 065	70	3 014	1 620	1 522	1 218	660	3 120	67 010	71 819
Agriculture as a percentage of:																	
National Gross Value Added at																	
market prices (a)	1.0	1.7	0.7	4.7	3.2	1.8	1.8	2.2	0.5	2.1	1.0	2.0	0.5	0.5	0.4	1.7	1.4
national employment (b)	1.9	3.5	2.5	16.5	6.2	3.9	7.6	4.8	2.4	3.2	5.9	11.9	5.0	2.4	1.4	4.7	4.0
Total labour input '000 AWUs (c)	74	76	646	577	947	1 015	186	1 187	4	220	172	536	109	73	338	5 673	6 160

Source: Eurostat

(a) Differs from agriculture's contribution to total economy Gross Value Added at current prices (tables 2.2 and 2.3) because it excludes directly paid subsidies.

(b) Source: Eurostat E-1 (labour force survey).

(c) Differs from workforce in agriculture in tables 2.2, 2.3 and 3.5 which is shown as '000 persons. In this table the basis is annual work units (full-time equivalents) as opposed to persons employed.

Table 2.6 Agriculture in the economy: Eurostat income indicators

Inquiries: Christine Jeannette on 01904 455080   email: christine.jeannette@defra.gsi.gov.uk

Average Index 1994-1996 = 100   Calendar years

	1990	1991	1992	1993	1994	1995	1996	1997	1998	1999	2000	2001
Net Value Added at factor cost of agriculture per total annual work unit (Indicator A)												
UK	71.3	70.1	76.4	90.2	95.6	105.5	98.8	76.7	65.8	64.5	58.5	60.5
EU-15	..	..	..	..	95.1	100.3	104.6	107.6	106.1	105.0	108.8	112.1
Net agricultural entrepreneurial income per unpaid annual work unit (Indicator B)												
UK	50.9	53.0	64.9	88.7	94.7	108.1	97.2	62.7	45.5	43.9	33.5	37.1
EU-15	..	..	..	..	..	..	..	..	..	..	..	..
Net entrepreneurial income from agriculture (Indicator C)												
UK	53.2	55.1	67.2	91.6	96.2	107.9	95.9	61.4	44.0	41.1	30.3	33.0
EU-15	..	..	..	..	95.8	100.6	103.6	102.1	94.7	88.2	86.6	88.5

Source: Eurostat

2002

Table 2.7 Net Farm Income by country and type of farm

Inquiries: Sophie Cruickshank 020 7238 3268 email: sophie.cruickshank@defra.gsi.gov.uk

Average net farm income per farm (£ thousand/farm)   Accounting years ending on average in February

	1994/95	1995/96	1996/97	1997/98	1998/99	1999/00	2000/01	2001/02	2002/03 (provisional) (a)
At current prices									
England									
dairy	36.3	41.1	33.6	22.0	13.5	9.0	10.8	22.8	17.0
cattle and sheep (LFA) (b)	13.1	17.2	17.4	10.7	5.7	4.6	6.7	9.7	25.0
cattle and sheep (lowland)	10.4	10.8	9.5	1.1	0.9	0.6	-0.4	-0.5	8.0
cereals	31.7	49.6	43.9	16.8	8.9	13.5	7.3	4.1	9.5
general cropping	72.2	89.1	47.6	23.1	36.0	8.8	18.4	17.9	17.5
pigs and poultry	31.5	67.3	60.9	20.4	-15.8	-5.3	37.9	21.8	30.0
mixed	34.2	51.8	39.6	8.9	1.6	9.4	9.7	5.5	15.5
Wales									
dairy	29.7	51.8	45.8	32.9	18.5	18.2	15.4	29.6	27.0
cattle and sheep (LFA) (b)	5.6	16.1	12.6	7.6	3.6	2.5	3.0	1.7	10.0
cattle and sheep (lowland)	6.1	12.4	8.9	2.3	-0.9	0.4	0.5	2.2	9.5
Scotland									
dairy	19.1	23.0	19.7	8.7	2.8	0.9	13.9	33.1	41.5
cattle and sheep (LFA) (b)	10.9	12.5	15.8	6.8	4.0	2.3	5.6	5.8	19.0
cereals	16.3	28.1	27.9	0.6	0.2	10.6	-0.5	-0.6	-7.5
general cropping	28.0	25.2	11.1	0.0	9.8	2.1	5.1	8.0	-2.5
mixed	23.3	30.8	25.7	-3.8	2.0	5.2	6.6	12.6	20.5
Northern Ireland									
dairy	23.2	32.1	20.8	11.8	8.6	8.3	14.9	17.5	10.5
cattle and sheep (LFA) (b)	5.6	6.6	6.8	3.5	0.3	-1.8	0.9	4.0	2.5
United Kingdom									
dairy	33.7	41.2	33.4	21.3	12.8	9.5	12.4	23.2	18.0
cattle and sheep (LFA) (b)	7.5	11.6	11.5	6.2	3.0	1.8	3.8	4.8	13.0
cattle and sheep (lowland)	7.9	8.6	7.0	0.7	-0.2	-	-0.1	0.4	7.5
cereals	34.5	54.6	48.6	16.6	8.4	13.4	6.8	3.3	7.0
general cropping	74.8	87.4	45.3	19.8	34.7	7.8	18.8	15.7	13.0
pigs and poultry	26.7	56.8	51.5	17.6	-17.6	-4.6	33.7	19.7	26.5
mixed	31.7	46.5	35.5	5.5	1.3	5.6	8.8	6.4	15.0
all types (excluding horticulture)	29.2	39.2	30.6	13.4	8.9	6.6	8.4	10.1	13.0
In real terms (at 2001/02 prices)									
United Kingdom									
dairy	40.4	47.8	37.8	23.3	13.6	9.9	12.6	23.2	18.0
cattle and sheep (LFA)	9.0	13.4	13.0	6.8	3.2	1.9	3.9	4.8	13.0
cattle and sheep (lowland)	9.4	9.9	8.0	0.7	-0.3	-	-	0.4	7.5
cereals	41.4	63.3	55.0	18.2	8.9	14.0	6.9	3.3	7.0
general cropping	89.6	101.3	51.3	21.7	36.9	8.2	19.1	15.7	13.0
pigs and poultry	32.0	65.9	58.3	19.3	-18.7	-4.8	34.2	19.7	26.0
mixed	38.0	54.0	40.2	6.0	1.3	5.8	8.9	6.4	15.0
all types (excluding horticulture)	35.1	45.4	34.6	14.7	9.4	6.9	8.6	10.1	13.0

source: Defra website, www.defra.gov.uk/esg

(a) Excluding farms subjected to compulsory Foot and Mouth Disease
    cull.

(b) Less Favoured Areas.

Chapter **3** The structure of the industry

Introduction **1** The tables in this chapter show the size and structure of the UK agricultural industry in 2002 and earlier years. Together they provide information on land use (chart 3.1) and livestock numbers in UK agriculture, the distribution of these between holdings, the industry's labour force and fixed capital.

Chart 3.1 Agricultural land use

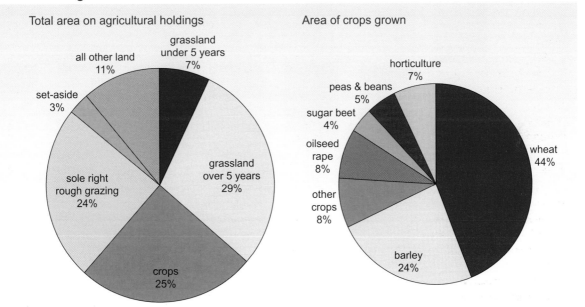

Land use, crop areas and livestock numbers
(Tables 3.1 and 3.2, Charts 3.2 and 3.3)

2 Changes in crop areas between 2001 and 2002 are shown in chart 3.2 and livestock numbers in chart 3.3.

3 Between June 2001 and June 2002, the total cattle population declined by 2.4 per cent following a 4.8 per cent fall the preceding year. The dairy herd fell by 1.1 per cent while the beef breeding herd fell by 3.0 per cent.

4 The total number of sheep and lambs fell by a further 2.4 per cent between June 2001 and June 2002 following a 13 per cent fall the preceding year. The breeding flock fell by 1.6 per cent, continuing the decline since 1999.

5 The total number of pigs fell by 4.4 per cent between June 2001 and June 2002. The pig breeding herd - sows in pig, other sows for breeding and gilts in pig - fell by 6.9 per cent due primarily to the long-term contraction of the breeding herd since 1997.

6 At June 2002, the total area of agricultural land was 18.4 million hectares, some 77 per cent of the total land area in the UK. The June 2002 Census showed an increase of 2.6 per cent in the area of crops in the UK. The total area of cereals increased by 7.7 per cent following a 10 per cent fall the preceding year. The area of wheat increased by 22 per cent while the area of barley fell by 12 per cent.

Chart 3.2 Changes in crop area

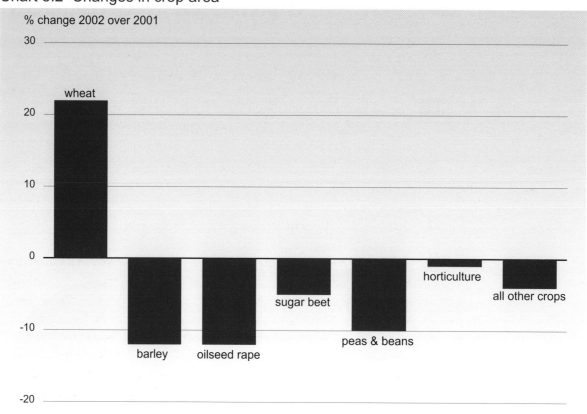

Chart 3.3 Changes in livestock numbers

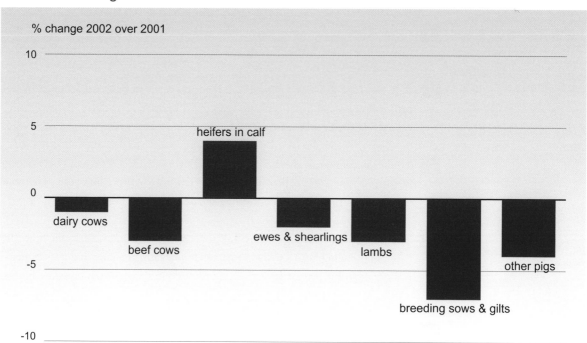

Numbers and sizes of holdings and enterprises
(Tables 3.3 and 3.4)

7 Tables 3.3 and 3.4 compare numbers and sizes of holdings and enterprises for 2000 (the most recent year for which data are available) with five years previously. Data for later years will be published on the Defra website as soon as possible.

8 European size units (ESUs) measure the financial potential of the holding in terms of the margins which might be expected from crops and stock. The margins used are gross margins standardised at average 1987-89 values. The threshold of 8 ESU is judged to be the minimum for full-time holdings. The tables confirm that the trend for larger holdings and enterprises has been maintained.

Labour force in agriculture
(Table 3.5)

9 Following the June Census 2000, an exercise to improve the register of agricultural holdings was undertaken in England. Two sets of results are shown for June 2001, including and excluding the effects of the exercise. June 2002 is directly comparable with June 2001(b) and shows a fall in the total labour force of 3.1 per cent.

Fixed capital stock
(Table 3.6)

10 Table 3.6 provides information on the volume of gross stock of fixed capital (excluding land and livestock) available to the agricultural industry. The figures are shown before allowing for depreciation and give a broad indication of how this aspect of the industry's productive capacity has changed over the years. Agriculture's total volume of fixed capital stock is estimated to have been 1.7 per cent lower at the end of 2002 compared to the end of 2001. This is a decline of around 9.7 per cent on the 1991-93 average level. In recent years, buildings and works, and plant and machinery, have shown a reduction in fixed capital stock while that of vehicles has remained relatively stable.

2002

Table 3.1 Agricultural land use

Inquiries: Miles Templeton 01904 455306   email: miles.h.templeton@defra.gsi.gov.uk

The data in this table cover all holdings (including minor holdings) in all four countries of the UK. (a)

Thousand hectares   At June of each year

	Average of 1991-1993	1998	1999	2000	2001	2002
Total agricultural area (total area on agricultural holdings plus common rough grazing)	18 864	18 604	18 579	18 311	18 556	18 388
This comprises:						
crops	4 819	4 971	4 709	4 665	4 455	4 573
bare fallow	57	34	33	37	43	33
Total tillage	4 876	5 005	4 742	4 702	4 498	4 605
all grass under five years old	1 591	1 301	1 226	1 226	1 205	1 230
Total arable land	6 467	6 306	5 968	5 928	5 703	5 835
all grass five years old and over (excluding rough grazing)	5 293	5 364	5 449	5 363	5 584	5 422
Total tillage and grass (b)	11 761	11 671	11 417	11 291	11 287	11 257
sole right rough grazing	4 924	4 621	4 575	4 445	4 435	4 484
set-aside	312	313	572	567	800	611
all other land (c) and woodland	637	773	789	780	801	802
Total area on agricultural holdings	17 633	17 377	17 352	17 083	17 323	17 154
common rough grazing (estimated)	1 231	1 227	1 227	1 228	1 232	1 234

source: Defra website, www.defra.gov.uk/esg

(a) From 2000 Scottish minor holdings have been included; data for earlier years are therefore not directly comparable. Also, from 1997 the Northern Ireland census was based on an improved register of holdings and included all active farms having one or more hectares of farmed land plus any below that size which had significant agricultural output. Figures for years before 1997 were revised to be comparable with later years.

(b) Includes bare fallow.

(c) In Great Britain other land comprises farm roads, yards, buildings (excluding glasshouses), ponds and derelict land.

Table 3.2 Crop areas and livestock numbers

Inquiries: Miles Templeton 01904 455306 email: miles.h.templeton@defra.gsi.gov.uk
The data in this table cover all holdings (including minor holdings) in all four countries of the UK. (a) (b)

At June of each year

		Average of 1991-1993	1998	1999	2000	2001	2002
Crop areas ('000 hectares)							
Total		4 819	4 971	4 709	4 665	4 455	4 573
This comprises:							
Total cereals		3 341	3 418	3 141	3 348	3 014	3 245
of which:	wheat	1 936	2 045	1 847	2 086	1 635	1 996
	barley	1 287	1 253	1 179	1 128	1 245	1 101
	oats	99	98	92	109	112	126
	rye and mixed corn	11	11	10	10	7	9
	triticale	9	11	13	16	14	14
Other arable crops (excluding potatoes)		1 106	1 209	1 211	979	1 103	993
of which:	oilseed rape	413	507	417	332	404	357
	sugar beet not for stockfeeding	197	189	183	173	177	169
	hops	4	3	3	2	2	2
	peas for harvesting dry and field beans	218	213	202	208	276	249
	linseed (c)	129	100	209	71	31	12
	other crops	146	199	197	192	214	204
Potatoes		176	164	178	166	165	158
Horticulture		196	180	179	172	173	176
of which:	vegetables grown in the open	133	125	126	119	120	124
	orchard fruit (d)	33	30	28	28	28	26
	soft fruit (e)	14	10	9	10	9	9
	ornamentals (f)	14	14	13	14	14	15
	glasshouse crops	2	2	2	2	2	2
Livestock numbers ('000 head)							
Total cattle and calves		11 926	11 519	11 423	11 135	10 602	10 345
of which:	dairy cows	2 707	2 439	2 440	2 336	2 251	2 227
	beef cows	1 739	1 947	1 924	1 842	1 708	1 657
	heifers in calf	769	787	763	718	701	728
Total sheep and lambs		44 381	44 471	44 656	42 264	36 716	35 834
of which:	ewes and shearlings (g)	. .	21 260	21 458	20 449	17 921	17 630
	lambs under one year old	22 405	22 138	22 092	20 857	17 769	17 310
Total pigs		7 751	8 146	7 284	6 482	5 845	5 588
of which:	sows in pig and other sows for breeding	690	675	603	537	527	483
	gilts in pig	112	103	85	73	71	74
Total fowl (h)		127 987	147 609	149 867	154 504	163 875	155 005
of which:	table fowl including broilers	76 600	98 244	101 625	105 689	112 531	105 137
	laying fowl (i)	32 965	29 483	29 258	28 687	29 895	28 778
	growing pullets	10 901	9 860	9 583	9 461	9 367	9 784

source: Defra website, www.defra.gov.uk/esg

continued

Table 3.2 continued

(a) For various reasons, the crop area figures and livestock numbers shown in this table may differ slightly from those shown in chapter 5.

(b) From 2000 Scottish minor holdings have been included; data for earlier years are therefore not directly comparable.

(c) England and Wales only prior to 1992.

(d) Includes non-commercial orchards.

(e) Includes wine grapes.

(f) Hardy nursery stock, bulbs and flowers.

(g) Improvements to the questions on sheep were introduced in 1995; data for earlier years are therefore not directly comparable.

(h) Improvements to the census methodology were introduced in 1997 to account for poultry production on unregistered units. The figures from 1997 onwards are not directly comparable with those for earlier years.

(i) Excludes fowls laying eggs for hatching.

Table 3.3 Numbers and sizes of holdings

Inquiries: Miles Templeton on 01904 455306 email: miles.h.templeton@defra.gsi.gov.uk
The data in this table exclude minor holdings in Great Britain. In Northern Ireland all active farms are included. (a)

At June of each year

		1995		2000	
		Number of holdings ('000)	Percent of total ESU	Number of holdings ('000)	Percent of total ESU
Size of holding (ESU) (b) (c)	under 8 ESU	103.0	2.9	112.3	2.7
	8 to under 40 ESU	68.1	16.3	60.8	14.6
	40 to under 100 ESU	42.5	31.3	38.0	28.8
	100 to under 200 ESU	15.7	24.6	15.9	25.6
	200 ESU and over	5.7	25.0	6.3	28.2
	Total	234.9	100.0	233.2	100.0
	average size (ESUs):				
	all holdings		36.8		36.3
	holdings 8 ESU and over		63.6		68.1
		Number of holdings ('000)	Hectares ('000)	Number of holdings ('000)	Hectares ('000)
Total area on holdings (b)	under 20 hectares	95.6	812	107.2	724
	20 to under 50 hectares	57.7	1 902	48.2	1 597
	50 to under 100 hectares	41.2	2 927	37.1	2 648
	100 hectares and over	40.5	11 359	40.7	11 571
	Total	234.9	16 999	233.2	16 540
	average area (hectares):				
	all holdings		72.4		70.9
	holdings 8 ESU and over		113.2		119.1
	% of total area on holdings				
	with 100 hectares and over		66.8		70.0
		Number of holdings ('000)	Hectares ('000)	Number of holdings ('000)	Hectares ('000)
Tillage and grass area (b)(d)(e)	0.1 to under 20 hectares	95.0	796	97.3	699
	20 to under 50 hectares	58.1	1 915	48.7	611
	50 to under 100 hectares	40.3	2 842	36.3	2 584
	100 hectares and over	30.0	5 775	31.3	6 202
	Total	223.3	11 329	213.6	11 096
	average crops and grass area per holding (f)		50.7		52.0
	% of total crops and grass area on holdings with 100 hectares and over		51.0		55.9

source: Defra website, www.defra.gov.uk/esg

(a) From 1997 the Northern Ireland census was based on an improved register of holdings and included all active farms having one or more hectares of farmed land plus any below that size which had significant agricultural output.

(b) Land in Great Britain let out under short-term lets is attributed to the lessor, but land so let out in Northern Ireland (under the conacre system) is now attributed to the lessee. This difference affects both the number of holdings and their average size.

(c) European Size Units (ESU) measure the financial potential of the holding in terms of the margins which might be expected from the crops and stock. The margins used are grossed margins

standardised at average 1987-89 values. The threshold of 8 ESU is judged to be the minimum for full-time holdings.

(d) The numbers of holdings shown in this part of the table are lower than those presented in the "total area" part of the table because holdings without crops and grass are excluded.

(e) The areas shown in this part of the table exclude set-aside land.

(f) Refers to holdings with crops and grass.

2002

Table 3.4 Numbers and sizes of enterprises

Inquiries: Miles Templeton on 01904 455306 email: miles.h.templeton@defra.gsi.gov.uk
The data in this table exclude minor holdings in Great Britain. In Northern Ireland all active farms are included. (a)

Areas refer to the area of the specified crop and not to the area of the holding   At June of each year

		1995		2000	
		Number of holdings ('000)	Hectares ('000)	Number of holdings ('000)	Hectares ('000)
Cereals (excluding maize)	under 20 hectares	34.4	302	28.3	259
	20 to under 50 hectares	18.8	612	16.0	524
	50 hectares and over	19.6	2 262	20.7	2 560
	Total	72.7	3 176	65.0	3 344
	Average area (hectares) (b)		43.7		51.4
	% of total cereals area on holdings				
	with 50 hectares and over		71.2		76.6
Oilseed rape	under 20 hectares	8.7	92	7.3	80
	20 to under 50 hectares	4.8	146	4.4	135
	50 hectares and over	1.5	116	1.4	118
	Total	14.9	354	13.1	332
	Average area (hectares) (b)		23.7		25.5
	% of total oilseed rape area on holdings				
	with 50 hectares and over		32.7		35.6
Sugar beet (England and Wales only)	under 10 hectares	3.9	22	3.3	19
	10 to under 20 hectares	2.7	38	2.4	34
	20 hectares and over	3.1	136	2.8	119
	Total	9.7	196	8.6	173
	Average area (hectares) (b)		20.2		20.2
	% of total sugar beet area on				
	holdings with 20.0 hectares and over		69.5		69.1
Potatoes	under 10 hectares	14.4	42	9.5	29
	10 to under 20 hectares	2.9	41	2.6	37
	20 hectares and over	2.3	87	2.3	100
	Total	19.6	169	14.4	166
	Average area (hectares) (b)		8.6		11.5
	% of total potato area on holdings				
	with 20 hectares and over		51.3		60.2

		1995		2000	
		Number of holdings ('000)	Number of livestock ('000)	Number of holdings ('000)	Number of livestock ('000)
Dairy cows	1 to 49 dairy cows	17.4	468	12.8	316
	50 to 99	13.7	973	11.0	793
	100 and over	7.8	1 159	8.0	1 226
	Total	38.9	2 600	31.9	2 335
	Average size of herd		66.8		73.3
	% of total dairy cows in herds				
	of 100 and over		44.6		52.5
Beef cows	1 to 19 beef cows	42.9	329	36.9	297
	20 to 49	18.2	565	18.0	563
	50 and over	9.9	891	10.5	969
	Total	71.0	1 786	65.4	1 829
	Average size of herd		25.2		28.0
	% of total beef cows in herds				
	of 50 and over		49.9		53.0

continued

Table 3.4 continued

		1995		2000	
		Number of holdings ('000)	Number of livestock ('000)	Number of holdings ('000)	Number of livestock ('000)
Sheep breeding flock	1 to 99 breeding sheep	38.4	1 599	35.1	1 432
	100 to 499	34.4	7 983	31.6	7 479
	500 and over	10.8	9 786	11.2	10 520
	Total	83.6	19 369	77.9	19 432
	Average size of flock		231.6		249.4
	% of total breeding sheep in flocks of 500 and over		50.5		54.1
Pig breeding herd	1 to 49 breeding pigs	6.6	63	5.0	41
	50 to 99	0.9	66	0.6	9
	100 and over	2.1	613	1.5	527
	Total	9.7	742	7.1	607
	Average size of herd		76.7		85.4
	% of total breeding pigs in herds of 100 and over		82.6		86.8
Fattening pigs (Fattening pigs of over 20kg liveweight excluding barren sows)	1 to 199 fattening pigs	6.1	247	4.9	158
	200 to 999	2.9	1 437	2.0	1 043
	1,000 and over	1.3	2 942	1.2	2 840
	Total	10.3	4 626	8.1	4 041
	Average size of herd		450.7		501.3
	% of total fattening pigs in herds of 1,000 and over		63.6		70.3
Broilers (Includes small numbers of other table fowl in Scotland and Northern Ireland)	1 to 9,999 broilers	1.2	921	0.8	687
	10,000 to 99,999	0.8	33 457	0.9	36 656
	100,000 and over	0.2	42 199	0.3	67 960
	Total	2.3	76 577	2.0	105 303
	Average size of flock		33 869		53 508
	% of total broilers in flock of 100,000 and over		55.1		64.5
Laying fowls	1 to 4,999 laying fowls	27.7	2 574	23.8	2 056
	5,000 to 19,999	0.6	5 919	0.6	5 671
	20,000 and over	0.3	31 154	0.3	28 821
	Total	28.6	39 648	24.7	36 548
	Average size of flock		1 385		1 482
	% of total laying fowls in flocks of 20,000 and over		78.6		78.9

source: Defra website, www.defra.gov.uk/esg

(a) Improvements were introduced in 1997 to census methodology to account for production on unregistered units, therefore data for 1998 onwards are not directly comparable with years previous to 1998.

(b) Average area refers to the average area of the specified crop on holdings that grow that crop. Holdings that do not grow the crop are excluded from the calculation.

Table 3.5 Labour force in agriculture

Inquiries: Lindsey Clothier 01904 455319 email: lindsey.j.clothier@defra.gsi.gov.uk

The data cover main and minor holdings in the United Kingdom. (a) to (e)

At June of each year

	Average of 1991-1993	1999	2000	2001(a)	2001(b)	2002(b)
Workers						
Regular whole-time:						
male	100	82	73	69	70	65
female	15	12	10	11	11	11
Total	115	94	84	80	82	76
Regular part-time: (f)						
male	30	27	25	22	23	22
female	26	22	21	19	19	18
Total	56	50	45	41	42	40
Seasonal or casual:						
male	54	51	46	45	45	46
female	32	21	18	19	19	18
Salaried managers (g)	8	14	11	13	14	13
Total workers	265	230	204	198	202	194
Farmers, partners, directors and spouses						
whole-time	..	177	169	166	168	164
part-time (f)	..	179	183	186	198	193
Total farmers, partners, directors and spouses	373	356	353	352	367	356
Total labour force (including farmers and their spouses) (h) (i)	637	586	557	550	568	550

source: Defra website, www.defra.gov.uk/esg

(a) These results exclude the effect of the register improvement in England and are directly comparable with years prior to June 2001.

(b) These results include the effect of the register improvement in England and are NOT directly comparable to years prior to June 2001.

(c) From 1997 the Northern Ireland census has been based on an improved register of farm businesses and included all active farms having one or more hectares of farmed land plus any below that size which had significant agricultural output.

(d) Results from 1998 are not consistent with previous years due to changes in the labour questions on the June Agricultural and Horticultural Census, and revisions made to English and Welsh results.

(e) From 1998 estimates for holdings in England and Wales which have not been recording labour have been made, apart from economically insignificant holdings which are very unlikely to be in commercial production. An offsetting adjustment has been made to take out any labour being recorded on these very small holdings. The net effect has been to reduce the level of the labour series between 1998 and 2000 by about 5,000 workers. This has not affected the trends previously recorded.

(f) Part-time is defined as less than 39 hours per week in England and Wales, less than 38 hours per week in Scotland and less than 30 hours per week in Northern Ireland.

(g) From 1998 all farmers managing holdings for limited companies or other institutions in England and Wales were asked to classify themselves as salaried managers.

(h) This is the series referred to as 'Workforce in agriculture' in Table 2.2.

Table 3.6 Fixed capital stock of agriculture

Inquiries: Christine Jeannette on 01904 455080 email: christine.jeannette@defra.gsi.gov.uk
Excludes livestock capital assets

Indices 1995 = 100   At end year

	Average of 1991-1993	1998	1999	2000	2001	2002 (provisional)
Gross capital stock						
Buildings and works	99.5	97.4	95.4	93.3	91.5	..
Plant and machinery	99.8	96.7	94.0	91.3	89.2	..
Vehicles	93.3	104.0	103.2	102.9	103.2	..
Total	99.4	97.4	95.3	93.0	91.2	89.7

source: Defra website, www.defra.gov.uk/esg

Chapter **4** Prices

Price indices
(Table 4.1 and chart 4.1)

Price indices: crops and livestock
1995 = 100

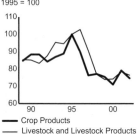

— Crop Products
— Livestock and Livestock Products

1 Table 4.1 shows price indices for agricultural products and inputs while chart 4.1 portrays the main changes in these indices over recent years. Between 2001 and 2002 the average price of agricultural products fell by 3.0 per cent whereas the average price of inputs remained almost unchanged. Since 1995 product prices have fallen by 22 per cent with the largest falls being in the prices of root crops (55 per cent) and cereals (43 per cent). The average price of inputs is marginally higher than in 1995, having risen by 1.9 per cent.

2 In 2002 the price of crop products fell by 5.7 per cent mainly due to falls of 11 per cent in the price of cereals and 19 per cent in the price of root crops; these falls were not offset by an increase of 13 per cent in the price of fresh fruit.

3 The price of livestock and livestock products fell by 2.5 per cent with a significant fall of 11 per cent in the price of milk and a fall of 7.0 per cent in the price of other livestock products. Livestock (for slaughter and export) prices rose by 2.0 per cent and egg prices by 4.3 per cent.

Chart 4.1 Price indices for products and inputs

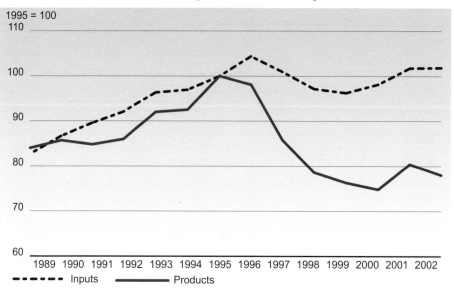

4 It should be noted that these indices are constructed using fixed annual weights (relating to 1995). They reflect observed market prices and do not take account of direct subsidy payments. In contrast, the price changes presented in table 6.2, derived from the aggregate accounts, include subsidy payments and are based on current production. For these reasons the price movements presented here and in Chapter 6 may differ.

Farm rents
(Table 4.2)

5 Table 4.2 shows indices of average rents per hectare. The rents refer to the calendar year, whilst the surveys on which they are based are conducted in October. Because of the duration of periods for rent settings, the values applying to the calendar year

2002

are deemed to be mainly (approximately 75 per cent) a carry over from those recorded in the preceding October. Therefore the derivation of the changes (noted below) are driven primarily by developments in 2001 and only to a lesser extent (approximately 25 per cent) by conditions in 2002.

6   For Great Britain as a whole provisional results for 2002 suggest an increase in average rents of around 2.2 per cent. Average rents increased in England by around 0.6 per cent while rents in Wales increased by around 17 per cent. Provisional results for Scotland and Northern Ireland show no change.

7   In England and Wales average rent estimates for the Full Agricultural Tenancies (FATs) series were based on results of the former annual Rent Enquiry (RE) for years up to and including 1995 and thereafter on the Annual Survey of Tenanted Land (ASTL). To ensure consistency with the earlier Rent Enquiry (RE) series, a weighted average of the RE and FATs rents derived from the ASTL has been taken for 1995 to 1997 (with an increasing incremental weighting on the ASTL). From 1998 the series is derived exclusively from the ASTL. Estimates of average rents in 2002 in England and Wales have been derived from a very small sample of ASTL returns and are thus purely provisional and will be subject to review when more robust estimates become available.

8   For Scotland, upto 1995, rent estimates were based on the results of continuing Field Enquiries. After its demise that year, they were based on the Farm Accounts Survey, and from 1998 on a new Survey of Tenanted Land.

9   In Northern Ireland virtually all land is let in "conacre", i.e. nominally short-term lettings (for 11 months or 364 days), although in practice some can be extended beyond this. The estimates are based on results from the Northern Ireland Farm Business Survey.

Agricultural land prices
(Table 4.3 and Chart 4.2)

10   The average prices of all sales shown in table 4.3 are obtained from data on land transfers collected by the Valuation Office Agency in Great Britain and the Valuation and Lands Agency in Northern Ireland. Only a very small proportion of the total area of farmland in the UK is sold in any particular year. The average price of land sold can therefore be subject to considerable variation from year to year, and in the case of the unweighted averages shown here, may vary with the size and type of plot sold in the year concerned. Chart 4.2 shows the average price in real terms of all sales of agricultural land from 1993-2001.

11   Recent data on land prices in Scotland should be treated with care given the substantial lags in gathering data. However, the available information on Scottish land sales suggests that average prices for all farm types rose in 2001. The upward trend in prices was somewhat unexpected given continuing depressed farm incomes and may suggest that subsidies are being capitalised into land values or that non-agricultural users are supporting land prices.

12   The average price of agricultural land in Wales has increased by 23 per cent (just over 15 per cent in real terms) over the period 1998 to 2001. This increase has occurred steadily over the period although it should be noted that a relatively small number of high (or low) value transactions can sometimes have a disproportionate

Chart 4.2 Prices of agricultural land (all sales) at 2001 prices

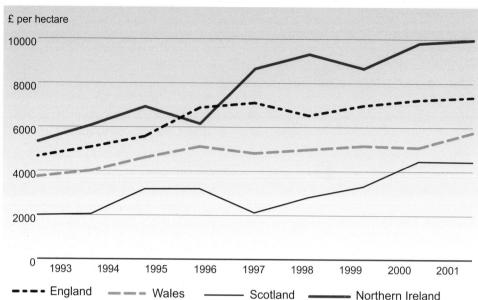

effect on this average. The number of transactions in Wales fell markedly in 2001. As in other parts of the UK, this was largely attributable to the Foot and Mouth Disease outbreak. This smaller number of transactions would have increased volatility in the average price for this year.

13   Provisional figures for England show that land prices were 3.6 per cent (1.7 per cent in real terms) higher in 2001, which year on year, is a much smaller increase than that seen in 2000. Looking at the data at a lower level shows the following: grade 3 land (moderate limitations to agricultural uses) saw the bulk of sales with an increase of 4.2 per cent; all other classes of land saw prices fall in 2001 compared to 2000. The price of ungraded land fell by 30 per cent, whereas grades 1 and 2 (none or few limitations to agricultural uses) fell by 1.3 per cent and grades 4 and 5 (severe limitations to agricultural uses) by 4.3 per cent. At a regional level, prices fluctuated with many areas seeing a decrease in land prices. Particularly interesting though, are Yorkshire and the Humber, the South West and the North West which saw noticeable increases (18 per cent, 17 per cent and 13 per cent respectively), these being some of the areas badly hit by Foot and Mouth Disease. Overall, the number of sales is still steadily decreasing (26 per cent), as is the area sold (23 per cent).

14   The number of land sales recorded each year in Northern Ireland has been declining markedly. Most sales involve relatively small areas and though variable, the long term trend in prices is upward.

Table 4.1 Price indices for products and inputs

Inquiries: Allan Howsam on 01904 455253 email: allan.howsam@defra.gsi.gov.uk

Indices: 1995=100 (a)

Average annual figures for calendar years

	Average of 1991-1993	1998	1999	2000	2001	2002 (provisional)
Producer prices for agricultural products (b)	87.6	78.6	76.3	74.8	80.4	78.0
of which:						
Crop products:	86.6	77.2	75.5	71.1	79.2	74.7
Cereals	103.0	68.3	66.5	59.9	64.6	57.2
Root crops	49.5	56.4	57.9	44.1	55.7	45.1
Fresh vegetables	88.4	96.8	90.6	94.9	104.3	103.7
Fresh fruit	98.7	99.6	93.8	101.7	97.3	110.1
Seeds	89.4	77.4	67.2	56.3	64.7	63.4
Flowers and plants	93.9	104.0	107.4	103.6	107.6	109.0
Other crop products	89.3	85.4	82.5	86.8	106.1	105.1
Livestock and livestock products:	88.8	77.0	74.0	74.3	78.5	76.5
Livestock (for slaughter and export)	91.9	76.2	74.3	78.2	79.2	80.8
Milk	82.4	77.7	73.6	67.9	77.2	68.8
Eggs	103.0	83.3	74.1	75.9	80.8	84.3
Other livestock products	83.8	74.7	71.4	69.8	75.3	70.1
Prices of agricultural inputs:	92.7	97.2	96.3	98.2	101.8	101.9
of which:						
Currently consumed in agriculture:	92.7	94.8	93.5	95.8	100.4	100.2
Livestock feedingstuffs	98.1	83.0	77.1	77.5	83.0	80.8
Seeds	92.3	91.7	83.2	76.3	82.2	81.2
Fertilisers and soil improvers	87.0	86.2	83.4	88.0	102.1	99.0
Plant protection products	95.5	98.0	96.4	89.9	87.7	86.3
Maintenance and repair of plant and machinery	90.1	112.5	116.6	120.9	126.2	132.5
Energy, lubricants	97.4	94.6	102.6	127.6	122.9	117.2
Maintenance and repair of buildings	88.4	103.8	102.8	105.3	107.3	109.6
Veterinary services	98.8	103.5	103.8	102.8	101.6	100.2
General expenses	88.8	105.5	109.4	112.4	118.7	119.5
Contributing to agricultural investment (c):	92.6	109.0	109.7	109.7	108.6	109.7
Machinery and other equipment	93.8	109.0	109.4	107.8	104.9	104.7
Buildings	89.1	109.1	110.8	115.2	118.9	124.1

source: Defra website, www.defra.gov.uk/esg

(a) Indices covering an aggregation of commodities are weighted averages with weights based on the values of output of the respective commodities in 1995.

(b) These indices reflect prices received by producers but exclude direct subsidies.

(c) Covers the purchase and maintenance of capital items, but excludes stocks.

Table 4.2 Farm rents

Inquiries: Michael Rowland on 01904 455557 email: michael.rowland@defra.gsi.gov.uk

Average per hectare: indices, 1995=100   Calendar years

		Average of 1991-1993	1998	1999	2000	2001	2002 (provisional)
England:	FATs (a)	95.5	114.0	112.7	112.4	108.2	100.4
	Average (b)	..	117.3	119.8	117.9	117.4	118.1
Wales:	FATs (a)	90.6	119.6	113.0	113.2	111.8	117.4
	Average (b)	..	126.1	126.1	129.1	141.4	165.1
Scotland (c)		70.1	121.0	123.5	128.5	127.9	127.9
Great Britain		91.9	118.3	120.6	119.5	120.0	122.6
Northern Ireland (d)		82.4	105.1	100.5	93.3	94.4	94.4

source: Defra website, www.defra.gov.uk/esg

(a) Average rent estimates for Full Agricultural Tenancies (FATs) up to 1995 were sourced from the Rent Enquiry (RE). For 1995 to 1997, a weighted average of RE and Annual Survey of Tenanted Land (ASTL) data was used. From 1998, estimates were sourced from the ASTL.

(b) A new series for England and Wales has been introduced giving a weighted average rent £/hectare for all agreements over a year in length.

(c) Scottish estimates relate to crops and grassland only. From 1998 onwards Crops and Grass is replaced by a Non-LFA classification.

(d) In Northern Ireland, virtually all land in let in 'conacre', i.e. nominally short-term lettings (for 11 months or 364 days).

Table 4.3 Agricultural land prices

Inquiries: Mark Hoult on 01904 455087 email: mark.a.hoult@defra.gsi.gov.uk

£ per hectare of all sales (a)   Calendar years

	Average of 1991-1993	1998	1999	2000	2001
England (b)	3 791	6 134	6 655	7 103	7 357
Wales (b)	3 011	4 686	4 917	4 991	5 760
Scotland	1 797	2 654	3 158	4 380	4 436
Northern Ireland	3 683	8 746	8 267	9 634	9 961

source: Defra website, www.defra.gov.uk/esg

(a) These series, based on Inland Revenue data, exclude land sold for non-agricultural purposes. In England, Wales and Scotland, sales of less than 5 hectares, and in Northern Ireland of less than 2 hectares, are also excluded. Data are subject to retrospective revision.

(b) From 1993, figures for England and Wales are not directly comparable with those estimated in previous years because some observations influenced by non-market considerations are now excluded.

Chapter **5** Commodities

Summary [1] The value of production (including subsidies directly related to products) was 1.1 per cent or £168 million higher at current prices in 2002. In this chapter the volume of production corresponds to the quantities of sales of products. It differs from the accounting concept of volume in chapter 6 which includes changes in work-in-progress and treats changes in quality as changes in volume.

- The total value of production of cereals increased by £169 million (8.4 per cent) to £2.2 billion. A partial recovery in areas and yields led to an increase in the volume of production of 22 per cent. Prices which recovered slightly in 2001 fell to new lows in 2002. Within the total, the value of production for wheat increased by 22 per cent whilst the value of barley declined by 14 per cent.

- The value of production of oilseed rape rose by £19 million (6.8 per cent) to £294 million. The volume of production increased and prices remained virtually unchanged from the previous year.

- The value of production of linseed fell by £10 million (64 per cent) to £5.7 million as a result of a 53 per cent decrease in the volume of harvested production and a reduction in the value of subsidies.

- Overall, total volume of production of potatoes (including seeds) fell in 2002 by 1.9 per cent, prices were lower than in 2001, and the value of production fell by 27 per cent to £463 million.

- The value of production for vegetables decreased by 8.0 per cent to £948 million. The value of production for ornamentals increased by 6.6 per cent to £726 million. The value of production of fruit rose by 9.4 per cent to £257 million owing to increased prices.

- The value of production of cattle and calves rose by 14 per cent in 2002 to £2.0 billion. This reflected a recovery in the production of beef and veal after the outbreak of Foot and Mouth Disease in 2001 and an increase in direct support payments.

- The value of production of sheep and lambs rose by 34 per cent to £840 million in 2002, again reflecting a recovery in the production of mutton and lamb following the outbreak of Foot and Mouth Disease in 2001 and an increase in direct support payments.

- The value of production of pigs fell by 8.3 per cent in 2002 to £687 million, due to weaker prices and a decline in clean pig marketings.

- The value of production of poultrymeat fell by 7.9 per cent to £1.2 billion, reflecting a 2.0 per cent fall in the volume of production and a 3.4 per cent fall in the average price for broilers. The increasing popularity for geese saw prices rise by 59 per cent.

- The value of production of livestock products (principally milk and eggs) fell by

8.0 per cent overall. The value of milk production fell by 12 per cent to £2.5 billion, following an 11 per cent fall in the average milk price received by farmers, while the value of production of eggs for human consumption increased by 17 per cent to £476 million, as buoyant domestic consumption increased egg prices and the volume of production.

- The cost of purchased feedingstuffs fell by £148 million or 6.4 per cent to £2.2 billion. The decrease was due to a decline in feed volumes in both the compound feed (except poultry) and straight feed sectors.

Structure of Tables `2` Each of the main commodity tables is divided, where appropriate, into three sections:

Production

For crops the aggregate areas and average yields are shown and are used to derive the levels of production. For livestock the populations, marketings and average slaughter weights are shown and lead to estimates of production. Value of production figures are broken down into sales out of the industry, sales within the industry, changes in stocks or work-in-progress and subsidies (less taxes) on production. The value of production in these tables is the same as the value of output in table 6.1.

Prices

Average producer prices and/or selected market prices are provided.

Supply and Use

Total new supply is defined as production plus imports less exports. Overseas trade statistics are provided by H.M. Customs and Excise.

Total domestic use is the total new supply adjusted for changes in stocks. Where stocks are insignificant or not known the total domestic use is assumed to be the same as the total new supply.

Production as percentage of total new supply for use in the *UK* gives an indication of the UK self-sufficiency in the commodity.

Cereals

Cereals `3`
(Tables 5.1-5.4)

The total value of production of cereals rose by 8.4 per cent to £2.2 billion. Plantings of wheat and winter barley increased sharply whilst the areas of spring barley and set-aside decreased. This reflected a return to more normal sowing patterns following the very wet planting conditions of the previous year's crops. The total area of cereals increased by 7.7 per cent and overall yields for cereals were up 13 per cent.

Monthly cereal price index
1995 average = 100

Wheat
(Table 5.2)

4   The value of wheat production increased by 22 per cent to £1.5 billion. An increase in production volume was partially offset by a fall in prices. Good planting and better growing conditions saw wheat area and yields return to near normal levels producing a 39 per cent increase in production. Subsidies increased by 29 per cent due to the larger area. Prices came under pressure from higher supplies and low export demand, falling by 13 per cent in 2002. Exports in 2001 were at their lowest level since 1983. In 2002 they increased slightly (by 6.5 per cent) though a full recovery was limited by tight supplies in the first half of the year and strong competition from other supplies in the second half of the year.

Barley
(Table 5.3)

5   The value of barley production fell by 14 per cent in 2002 to £623 million. This was due to a 7.6 per cent decrease in the volume of production, a decrease of 9.1 per cent in subsidies arising from a fall in area and a 5.5 per cent decrease in price. Intervention stocks increased to 134 thousand tonnes. Exports increased by 31 per cent in 2002 with higher sales to other European countries in the second half of the year.

Oats
(Table 5.4)

6   The value of oats production rose by 9.8 per cent in 2002 to £71 million. An increase in production was partially offset by falling prices. The volume of production increased by 23 per cent following increases in area and yields. Average prices fell by 16 per cent. Usage in 2002 increased by 4.0 per cent, whilst exports increased by around 34 per cent.

2002

Table 5.1 Total cereals

Inquiries: Alex Clothier on 01904 455068 email: alex.clothier@defra.gsi.gov.uk

Thousand tonnes (unless otherwise specified)   Calendar years

	Average of 1991-1993	1998	1999	2000	2001	2002 (provisional)
Production						
Area ('000 hectares)	3 341	3 418	3 141	3 348	3 014	3 245
Volume of harvested production	21 398	22 767	22 125	23 988	18 991	23 114
Value of production (£ million) (a)	2 587	2 502	2 326	2 337	2 023	2 192
Supply and use						
Production	21 398	22 767	22 125	23 988	18 991	23 114
Imports from: the EU	2 448	2 017	1 677	1 890	2 145	2 124
the rest of the world	520	739	926	914	838	788
Exports to: the EU	3 644	4 392	3 040	3 634	1 812	2 428
the rest of the world	1 903	1 418	1 360	1 995	613	357
Total new supply	18 820	19 714	20 329	21 163	19 549	23 241
Change in farm and other stocks	152	- 710	- 41	485	- 1 783	2 357
Total domestic uses	18 668	20 423	20 370	20 678	21 333	20 884
Production as % of total new supply for use in UK	114%	115%	109%	113%	97%	99%

source: Defra website, www.defra.gov.uk/esg

(a) Includes Arable Area Payments, but excludes set-aside payments
    and farm saved seed. Taxes, where applicable, are deducted.

Table 5.2 Wheat

Inquiries: Alex Clothier on 01904 455068 email: alex.clothier@defra.gsi.gov.uk

Thousand tonnes (unless otherwise specified)   Calendar years

	Average of 1991-1993	1998	1999	2000	2001	2002 (provisional)
Production						
Area ('000 hectares)	1 936	2 045	1 847	2 086	1 635	1 996
Yield (tonnes/hectare)	7.13	7.56	8.05	8.01	7.08	8.00
Volume of harvested production	13 783	15 449	14 867	16 704	11 573	16 053
Value of production (£ million) (a)	1 718	1 652	1 525	1 578	1 226	1 490
of which: sales	1 552	1 126	1 061	995	1 000	868
subsidies (b)	35	466	420	458	351	453
on farm use	97	79	64	40	38	39
change in stocks	34	- 18	- 20	84	- 162	131
Prices (£/tonne) (c)						
Milling wheat	134	84	81	74	82	71
Feed wheat	117	75	73	65	75	63
Supply and use						
Production	13 783	15 449	14 867	16 704	11 573	16 053
Imports from: the EU	926	779	579	556	725	745
the rest of the world	244	471	616	621	580	495
Exports to: the EU	2 634	3 566	2 598	2 957	1 257	1 462
the rest of the world	1 245	643	255	714	369	270
Total new supply	11 073	12 490	13 209	14 209	11 252	15 561
Change in farm and other stocks	256	- 429	29	1 079	- 2 144	2 594
Total domestic uses	10 817	12 919	13 180	13 130	13 396	12 967
of which: flour milling	5 018	5 707	5 668	5 617	5 667	5 627
animal feed	4 556	6 117	6 367	6 460	6 612	6 234
seed	326	332	375	265	298	300
other uses and waste	917	763	769	788	819	806
Production as % of total new supply for use in UK	124%	124%	113%	118%	103%	103%
% of home grown wheat in milling grist	81%	80%	83%	82%	85%	85%

Wheat (Crop Years: July-June)

Thousand tonnes (unless otherwise specified)   Crop years: July-June

	1997/98	1998/99	1999/00	2000/01	2001/02
Production and output					
Volume of harvested production	15 018	15 449	14 867	16 704	11 573
Value of production (£ million) (a)	1 762	1 593	1 508	1 533	1 285
of which: sales	1 179	1 075	1 033	1 053	834
subsidies (b)	493	466	420	458	351
on farm use	81	80	47	36	35
change in stocks	8	- 29	9	- 14	64

source: Defra website, www.defra.gov.uk/esg

(a) Excludes farm saved seed

(b) Includes Arable Area Payments but excludes set-aside payments and is net of taxes.

(c) Average prices weighted by volumes of sales.

Table 5.3 Barley

Inquiries: Alex Clothier on 01904 455068 email: alex.clothier@defra.gsi.gov.uk

Thousand tonnes (unless otherwise specified)   Calendar years

	Average of 1991-1993	1998	1999	2000	2001	2002 (provisional)
Production						
Area ('000 hectares)	1 287	1 253	1 179	1 128	1 245	1 101
Yield (tonnes/hectare)	5.44	5.29	5.58	5.76	5.39	5.62
Volume of harvested production	7 010	6 623	6 581	6 492	6 704	6 192
Value of production (£ million) (a)	805	781	735	686	725	623
of which: sales	570	397	308	312	284	291
subsidies (b)	35	277	259	244	260	236
on farm use	251	164	148	137	151	137
change in stocks	- 51	- 57	20	- 7	30	- 40
Prices (£/tonne) (c)						
Malting barley	124	85	79	75	77	73
Feed barley	112	71	70	65	67	58
Supply and use						
Production	7 010	6 623	6 581	6 492	6 704	6 192
Imports from: the EU	219	154	107	50	79	51
the rest of the world	3	31	22	20	21	34
Exports to: the EU	940	768	399	550	439	811
the rest of the world	657	775	1 105	1 281	244	86
Total new supply	5 635	5 264	5 206	4 731	6 121	5 380
Change in farm and other stocks	- 86	- 285	- 71	- 624	402	- 283
Total domestic uses	5 721	5 549	5 277	5 355	5 719	5 663
or which: brewing/distilling	1 857	1 999	1 910	1 925	1 974	1 953
animal feed	3 548	3 304	3 129	3 199	3 538	3 508
seed	179	200	192	187	160	160
other uses and waste	136	45	45	44	46	43
Production as % of total new supply for use in UK	124%	126%	126%	137%	110%	115%

Barley (Crop Years: July-June)

Thousand tonnes (unless otherwise specified)   Crop years: July-June

	1997/98	1998/99	1999/00	2000/01	2001/02
Production and output					
Volume of harvested production	7 828	6 623	6 581	6 492	6 704
Value of production (£ million) (a)	925	767	725	691	698
of which: sales	435	339	323	297	289
subsidies (b)	316	277	259	244	260
on farm use	175	155	141	142	150
change in stocks	- 1	- 4	1	7	-

source: Defra website, www.defra.gov.uk/esg

(a) Excludes farm saved seed

(b) Includes Arable Area Payments but excludes set-aside payments and is net of taxes.

(c) Average prices weighted by volumes of sales.

Table 5.4 Oats

Inquiries: Alex Clothier on 01904 455068 email: alex.clothier@defra.gsi.gov.uk

Thousand tonnes (unless otherwise specified)   Calendar years

	Average of 1991-1993	1998	1999	2000	2001	2002 (provisional)
Production						
Area ('000 hectares)	99	98	92	109	112	126
Yield (tonnes/hectare)	5.09	6.00	5.87	5.88	5.49	6.03
Volume of harvested production	501	586	541	640	616	758
Value of production (£ million) (a)	61	61	58	65	65	71
of which: sales:	39	25	24	27	29	28
subsidies (b)	3	22	20	23	23	28
on farm use	21	12	14	13	12	11
change in stocks	- 2	2	- 1	3	1	4
Prices (£/tonne) (c)						
Milling oats	118	66	71	64	69	58
Feed oats	117	62	71	65	68	58
Supply and use						
Production	501	586	541	640	616	758
Imports from: the EU	4	11	11	7	10	15
the rest of the world	1	-	2	-	-	-
Exports to: the EU	46	54	34	107	108	145
the rest of the world	-	-	-	-	-	-
Total new supply	461	543	519	540	518	628
Change in farm and other stocks	- 18	4	-	30	- 41	46
Total domestic uses	479	539	519	510	559	582
of which: milling	217	272	266	261	287	313
animal feed	227	246	229	231	252	249
seed	19	18	21	16	18	16
other uses and waste	16	3	3	3	3	4
Production as % of total new supply for use in UK	109%	108%	104%	119%	119%	121%

source: Defra website, www.defra.gov.uk/esg

(a) Excludes farm saved seed

(b) Includes Arable Area Payments but excludes set-aside payments and is net of taxes.

(c) Average prices weighted by volumes of sales.

Other crops

Oilseed rape
(Table 5.5)

Oilseed rape valuation
£ million

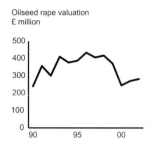

7 The value of production increased by 6.8 per cent to £294 million. The total area planted fell by 4.3 per cent and the split between winter and spring sowings returned to more typical levels after the very wet planting conditions of the previous year. However, better yields led to an overall increase in the volume of production of 24 per cent. Prices remained strong during the year giving an overall increase of 20 per cent in the value of sales. Overall subsidy payments fell by 22 per cent due to the reduced area and a reduction in the subsidy rate.

Linseed
(Table 5.6)

8 The value of production fell by 64 per cent to £6 million. A decrease in the planted area of 59 per cent was only slightly offset by a recovery in yield and gave a fall in production of 53 per cent. At 18 thousand tonnes, production has fallen to its lowest level since 1987. Subsidy payments fell by 73 per cent to £3 million.

Sugar beet and sugar
(Table 5.7)

9 The overall value of sugar beet production for 2002 rose by 6.3 per cent to £272 million. The area of contracted sugar beet decreased; however, an increase in yield led to a 13 per cent increase in the volume of production. The average sugar content was up on 2001 at 17.70 per cent. Sugar production from beet rose by 14 per cent to 1.4 million tonnes.

10 Northern Ireland area, yield and production data have been revised back to 2000.

Potatoes
(Table 5.8)

Potatoes: area and price

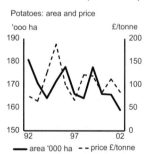

11 The total area for all potatoes fell by 4.1 per cent in 2002. The market for earlies continued to decline and the area for earlies fell by 3.9 per cent. The area for maincrop fell by 4.1 per cent. The value of production in 2002 fell by 27 per cent, owing to the average price paid to registered producers being lower than that obtained in 2001, especially for earlies.

Peas and beans for stockfeed
(Table 5.9)

12 The combined value of production for peas and beans for stockfeed fell by 12 per cent to £125 million. The area of dried peas grown for stockfeed fell by 19 per cent in 2002. Yields decreased slightly and production was down by 21 per cent. The area of field beans grown for stockfeed fell by 4.6 per cent in 2002; however, this was offset by an increase in yield to give a rise in the volume of production of 5.0 per cent.

Table 5.5 Oilseed rape

Inquiries: Melanie Riley on 01904 455067 email: melanie.riley@defra.gsi.gov.uk

Thousand tonnes (unless otherwise specified)   Calendar years

	Average of 1991-1993	1998	1999	2000	2001	2002 (provisional)
Production						
Area ('000 hectares)	426	534	537	402	451	432
Yield (tonnes/hectare)	2.80	2.94	3.23	2.88	2.56	3.33
Volume of harvested production	1 193	1 567	1 733	1 157	1 157	1 437
of which:						
Production not on set-aside land:						
Area ('000 hectares)	413	507	417	332	404	357
Yield (tonnes/hectare) (a)	2.84	2.95	3.24	2.90	2.57	3.49
Production (a)	1 175	1 494	1 353	965	1 038	1 245
Production on set-aside land:						
Area ('000 hectares)	41	27	120	70	48	75
Yield (tonnes/hectare)	1.37	2.67	3.17	2.76	2.48	2.54
Production	56	73	379	192	119	191
Value of production (£ million)	358	417	371	249	275	294
of which:						
sales	252	259	202	158	167	201
subsidies (b) (c)	162	155	175	110	103	81
change in stocks	- 3	3	- 6	- 19	4	12
Supply and use						
Production	1 193	1 567	1 733	1 157	1 157	1 437
Imports from: the EU	146	277	208	270	463	300
the rest of the world	46	49	115	18	142	92
Exports to: the EU	81	230	126	50	16	114
the rest of the world	22	46	149	-	-	50
Total new supply	1 282	1 616	1 785	1 395	1 746	1 665
Production as % of total new supply for use in UK	93%	97%	97%	83%	66%	86%

source: Defra website, www.defra.gov.uk/esg

(a) These figures are on the basis of a standard (9%) moisture content.

(b) Includes Arable Area Payments but excludes set-aside payments. Under the Arable Area Payments Scheme (AAPS) until 1999 payments were made to oilseed rape producers in two instalments: an advance payment in the autumn of the year of harvest and the balance in the following spring. However, for the purposes of these accounts all payments have been included under the year of harvest. From 2000, only one payment was made, in the year of harvest.

(c) In 2000, an area of genetically modified contaminated crop was destroyed. The subsidies valuation includes both the subsidy payment for this area and the compensation payments made.

Table 5.6   Linseed

Inquiries: Melanie Riley on 01904 455067 email: melanie.riley@defra.gsi.gov.uk

Thousand tonnes (unless otherwise specified)   Calendar years

	Average of 1991-1993	1998	1999	2000	2001	2002 (provisional)
Production						
Area ('000 hectares)	133	101	213	74	31	13
Yield (tonnes/hectare)	1.51	1.41	1.42	0.58	1.23	1.43
Volume of harvested production	194	143	302	43	39	18
of which:						
Production not on set-aside land:						
Area ('000 hectares)	129	99	209	72	31	12
Yield (tonnes/hectare) (a)	1.52	1.41	1.42	0.56	1.23	1.34
Production (a)	191	140	297	40	38	16
Production on set-aside land:						
Area ('000 hectares)	12	2	3	2	-	1
Yield (tonnes/hectare)	0.75	1.57	1.55	1.30	1.25	2.87
Production	9	3	5	3	1	2
Value of production (£ million)	102	68	132	34	16	6
of which: sales	21	20	29	8	6	3
subsidies (b)	81	48	102	29	10	3
change in stocks	-	1	2	-	-	-
Supply and use						
Production	194	143	302	43	39	18
Imports from: the EU	6	1	2	4	1	1
the rest of the world	1	37	1	3	25	22
Exports to: the EU	63	39	100	63	44	7
the rest of the world	1	1	6	1	-	-
Total new supply	136	141	199	- 14	20	34
Production as % of total new supply for use in UK	143%	101%	152%	-303%	191%	53%

source: Defra website, www.defra.gov.uk/esg

(a) These figures are based on a standard (9%) moisture content.

(b) Includes Arable Area Payments but excludes set-aside payments.

Table 5.7 Sugar beet and sugar

Inquiries: Karen Stark on 01904 455126 email: karen.p.stark@defra.gsi.gov.uk

Thousand tonnes (unless otherwise specified)   Calendar years

	Average of 1991-1993	1998	1999	2000	2001	2002 (provisional)
Sugar beet						
Area ('000 ha)	197	189	183	173	177	169
Yield (adjusted tonnes/hectare)	48.32	53.00	57.95	52.48	46.98	55.78
Volume of harvested production	9 505	10 002	10 584	9 079	8 335	9 435
Average market price (£/adjusted tonne) (a)	37	30	26	28	31	29
Value of production (£ million)	350	298	280	252	256	272
Sugar content %	17.11	17.34	17.16	17.10	17.16	17.70
Sugar ('000 tonnes refined basis)						
Production (b)	1 377	1 439	1 548	1 325	1 222	1 390
Imports from: the EU	127	156	117	143	120	186
the rest of the world	1 181	1 178	1 137	1 101	1 118	1 123
Exports to: the EU	86	84	83	90	94	104
the rest of the world	261	687	534	608	535	383
Total new supply	2 338	2 002	2 185	1 871	1 832	2 212
Production as % of total new supply for use in UK	59%	72%	71%	71%	67%	63%

source: Defra website, www.defra.gov.uk/esg

(a) Average price for all sugar beet, including transport allowance and bonuses.

(b) Sugar coming out of the factory in the early part of the new year is regarded as being part of the previous calendar year's production.

2002

Table 5.8   Potatoes

Inquiries: Melanie Riley on 01904 455067 email: melanie.riley@defra.gsi.gov.uk

Thousand tonnes (unless otherwise specified)   Calendar years

	Average of 1991-1993	1998	1999	2000	2001	2002 (provisional)
Production						
Area ('000 hectares)	176	164	178	166	166	159
of which: early	16	18	14	12	14	13
maincrop	160	146	164	154	152	146
Yield (tonnes/hectare):						
early	24.6	18.9	23.3	22.6	12.4	16.4
maincrop	41.8	41.6	41.6	41.4	41.7	42.3
overall	40.2	39.1	40.1	40.0	39.2	40.1
Volume of harvested production	7 085	6 422	7 131	6 636	6 498	6 375
of which: early	401	336	322	276	172	219
maincrop	6 684	6 086	6 809	6 359	6 326	6 156
End year stocks	3 668	3 349	3 706	3 062	3 557	3 589
Value of production (£ million)	484	630	750	454	637	463
of which: sales	457	660	678	499	568	447
on farm seed use	17	12	30	9	13	13
change in stocks	9	- 42	43	- 54	56	3
Prices (£/tonne) (a)						
Average price paid to registered producers for:						
early potatoes	107	152	75	132	184	110
maincrop potatoes	77	119	119	80	110	81
all potatoes	78	122	119	83	113	84
Supply and use						
Total production	7 085	6 422	7 131	6 636	6 498	6 375
Supplies from the Channel Islands	48	38	44	43	47	46
Imports	961	1 194	1 105	1 185	1 533	1 284
of which:						
early from:						
the EU	82	77	65	65	70	70
the rest of the world	148	124	128	81	95	95
maincrop from:						
the EU	74	197	69	166	468	197
the rest of the world	18	5	7	8	10	7
processed (raw equivalent) from:						
the EU	581	758	772	818	827	865
the rest of the world	29	16	44	17	25	13
seed from:						
the EU	29	17	19	30	38	38
the rest of the world	-	-	-	-	-	-

continued

Table 5.8 continued

	Average of 1991-1993	1998	1999	2000	2001	2002 (provisional)
Exports	252	375	339	369	350	363
of which:						
raw to:						
the EU	71	175	156	153	120	131
the rest of the world	47	8	3	8	2	5
processed (raw equivalent) to:						
the EU	67	84	82	93	113	117
the rest of the world	5	25	20	35	27	23
seed to:						
the EU	30	49	31	32	57	59
the rest of the world	32	34	46	48	30	28
Total new supply	7 841	7 279	7 941	7 494	7 727	7 342
Change in stocks	97	- 347	358	- 645	495	33
Total domestic uses	7 744	7 626	7 584	8 139	7 232	7 309
of which: used for human consumption	6 064	5 997	6 210	6 523	6 004	5 987
seed for home crops (including seed imports)	533	437	446	452	380	399
support buying	322	-	-	-	-	-
chats, waste and retained stockfeed	826	1 192	928	1 164	848	923
Production as % of total new supply for use in the UK	90%	88%	90%	89%	84%	87%

source: Defra website, www.defra.gov.uk/esg

Potatoes (Crop Years: June-May)

Thousand tonnes (unless otherwise specified)   Crop years: June-May

	1997/98	1998/99	1999/00	2000/01	2001/02
Production					
Volume of harvested production	7 128	6 422	7 131	6 636	6 498
Value of production (£ million)	476	853	450	624	544
of which: sales	463	829	438	603	531
on farm seed use	9	16	24	7	15
change in stocks	4	8	- 13	14	- 1
Prices (£/tonne)					
Average realised return (a)	81	159	74	116	96

source: Defra website, www.defra.gov.uk/esg

(a) Takes account of support buying, seed sales and sacks.

Table 5.9 Peas and beans for stockfeed

Inquiries: Karen Stark on 01904 455126 email: karen.p.stark@defra.gsi.gov.uk

Thousand tonnes (unless otherwise specified)   Calendar years

	Average of 1991-1993	1998	1999	2000	2001	2002 (provisional)
Peas for harvesting dry (a)						
Area ('000 hectares)	62	82	71	67	83	68
Yield (tonnes/hectare)	3.66	3.17	4.00	3.69	3.54	3.43
Volume of harvested production (a)	226	259	285	247	295	233
Value of production (£ million)	44	47	46	39	47	37
of which: sales	34	19	22	20	26	18
subsidies (b)	27	28	24	19	22	19
Field beans (mainly for stockfeed)						
Area ('000 hectares)	141	111	113	124	172	164
Yield (tonnes/hectare)	3.48	3.41	3.50	3.90	3.50	3.85
Volume of harvested production (a)	494	378	395	485	602	632
Value of production (£ million)	95	66	69	74	95	88
of which: sales	72	28	30	39	53	46
subsidies (b)	69	38	38	35	42	42

source: Defra website, www.defra.gov.uk/esg

(a) The figures presented here cover only that part of the crop which is assumed to be used for stockfeed (80% of total production); the remainder is included in Horticulture: vegetables, Table 5.10.

(b) Includes Arable Area Payments but excludes set-aside payments.

Horticulture

13 The total area devoted to horticulture as reported in the 2002 June Agricultural Census (table 3.2), was 176 thousand hectares, compared with 173 thousand hectares in 2001.

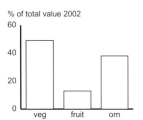

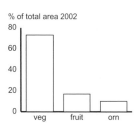

Vegetables
(Table 5.10)

14 The area of field vegetables rose by 5.3 per cent in 2002. The value of production decreased by 11 per cent. There was a fall of 31 per cent in the value of cabbages and 34 per cent in the value of carrots although the value of cauliflowers increased by 47 per cent. Good late growing conditions encouraged crops to bulk up with reported record yields for some crops, in particular carrots. The overall quality of the UK onion crop was very good. The value of mushrooms fell by 3.1 per cent as European suppliers were able to offer lower price mushrooms.

15 The area of protected vegetables fell by 2.6 per cent continuing the downward trend of the last few years. The value of production decreased by 2.1 per cent. The value of tomatoes increased by 5.5 per cent. There was an exceptional demand for salad crops. Growing conditions were favourable but returns to growers continued to be a major concern for the industry.

Fruit
(Table 5.11)

16 Orchard fruit area fell by 12 per cent in 2002 while the value of production fell by 20 per cent. The value of culinary apples fell by 7.3 per cent and that of dessert apples by 12 per cent. The value of production of pears fell by 3.4 per cent. Apples and pears found a firm market, although prices for some varieties have been below expectations, given the reduced level of UK fruit supply this year.

17 Soft fruit area fell by 9.5 per cent. The value of production rose by 32 per cent. The value of production for raspberries rose by 55 per cent and strawberries by 32 per cent. The sunny autumn boosted strawberry and raspberry yields compensating for the difficult growing conditions in May and June. Demand for both crops was good.

Ornamentals
(Table 5.12)

18 Value of production of the relatively small flowers and bulbs sector fell by 4.2 per cent. Sales of outdoor bulb flowers were difficult resulting in average prices. However, export sales of daffodil flowers remained strong. Cut flowers sales were steady and the quality continued to improve. However, competition from imports remained strong.

19 The value of production rose by 9.2 per cent. Over-supply of native trees and fierce import competition created further price sensitivity. Spring sales of container stock to the retail trade started well but were hampered by weather conditions. The wet conditions also delayed lifting of stock in the landscape/amenity sector.

Protected **20** The value for protected ornamentals rose by 4.0 per cent with sales of nursery stock
ornamentals   variable due to the poor weather. Some investment is being made in glass but
(Table 5.12)   imports remain a serious concern.

Table 5.10   Horticulture: vegetables

Inquiries: Lesly Lawton on 01904 455072 email: lesly.lawton@defra.gsi.gov.uk

Thousand tonnes (unless otherwise specified)   Calendar years

	Average of 1991-1993	1998	1999	2000	2001	2002 (provisional)
Production						
Area ('000 hectares):	178	160	149	137	136	143
of which: grown in the open (a) (b)	176	155	148	136	135	142
protected (c)	2	1	1	1	1	1
Value of production (£ million):	944	987	962	885	1 031	948
grown in the open	617	662	644	569	723	647
protected	327	324	318	316	308	301
of which: subsidies (d)	14	7	5	4	5	4
Selected crops:						
cabbages	65	59	55	49	62	43
carrots	73	88	94	72	163	107
cauliflowers	71	41	36	42	30	44
lettuces	112	95	103	82	107	104
mushrooms	152	174	170	150	150	146
peas	58	53	56	61	58	62
tomatoes	70	64	67	85	79	84
Prices (Farm gate price (£/tonne))						
Selected crops:						
cauliflowers	220	216	211	270	277	342
tomatoes	575	595	576	752	725	824
Supply and use (e)						
Total production	3 164	2 863	2 953	2 889	2 662	2 780
Supplies from the Channel Islands	23	16	16	15	15	15
Imports from: the EU	702	1 091	1 085	1 091	1 301	1 359
the rest of the world	209	154	163	159	186	211
Exports to: the EU	58	73	89	97	97	115
the rest of the world	6	5	3	2	6	11
Total new supply	4 034	4 046	4 125	4 054	4 061	4 239
Production as % of total new supply for use in the UK	78%	71%	72%	71%	66%	66%

source: Defra Statistics website, www.defra.gov.uk/esg

(a) Includes peas harvested dry for human consumption.

(b) Areas relate to field areas multiplied by the number of crops in the
year and hence differ from those shown in table 3.2.

(c) Excludes mushrooms area from 1992.

(d) Arable Area Payments for peas harvested dry.

(e) Trade figures relate to fresh produce where distinguishable.

Table 5.11 Horticulture: fruit

Inquiries: Lesly Lawton on 01904 455072 email: lesly.lawton@defra.gsi.gov.uk

Thousand tonnes (unless otherwise specified) — Calendar years

	Average of 1991-1993	1998	1999	2000	2001	2002 (provisional)
Production						
Area ('000 hectares):	44	36	34	38	37	33
of which: orchard fruit (a)	31	27	25	28	28	25
soft fruit (b)	13	9	9	10	10	9
End year stocks (c)	125	93	73	79	73	56
Value of production (£ million) (e):	279	259	257	229	235	257
of which: orchard fruit (d)	140	126	106	83	99	79
soft fruit	138	125	139	133	123	162
of which: sales	276	234	265	227	231	264
change in stocks (c)	3	24	- 8	2	5	- 7
Selected crops:						
dessert apples	64	47	59	36	37	33
culinary apples	36	29	28	23	19	17
pears	15	11	10	8	13	13
raspberries	30	35	37	26	22	35
strawberries	72	75	87	81	79	104
Prices (Farm gate price (£/tonne))						
Selected crops:						
dessert apples	407	480	437	358	354	387
culinary apples	196	341	249	215	176	189
pears	457	405	426	283	349	391
Supply and use (f)						
Total production	496	277	345	304	328	291
Supplies from the Channel Islands	20	16	16	15	15	15
Imports from: the EU	1 033	1 390	1 172	1 257	1 291	1 196
the rest of the world	1 198	1 408	1 517	1 497	1 589	1 647
Exports to: the EU	70	63	73	59	73	67
the rest of the world	4	7	1	-	1	1
Total new supply	2 662	3 022	2 975	3 013	3 149	3 081
Net change in stocks	7	44	- 20	6	- 6	- 18
Total domestic uses	2 655	2 978	2 995	3 007	3 155	3 099
Production as % of total new supply for use in the UK	19%	9%	12%	10%	10%	9%

source: Defra website, www.defra.gov.uk/esg

(a) Includes field area of commercial orchards only, and may therefore differ from the area in table 3.2, which also includes non-commercial orchards.

(b) Excludes area of wine grapes and may therefore differ from the area in table 3.2.

(c) Stocks relate to apples and pears.

(d) Excludes EC grubbing up grant.

(e) Includes glasshouse fruit.

(f) Trade figures relate to fresh produce where distinguishable.

Table 5.12 Horticulture: ornamentals

Inquiries: Lisa Szydlowska 01904 455070 email: lisa.szydlowska@defra.gsi.gov.uk

Calendar year

	Average of 1991-1993	1998	1999	2000	2001	2002 (provisional)
Production						
Area ('000 hectares) (a)	19	19	20	21	19	20
Value of production (£ million)	539	650	714	674	681	726
of which: flowers and bulbs in the open (b)	48	38	34	33	32	31
hardy ornamental nursery stock	268	352	400	374	392	428
protected crops	224	260	280	268	257	267
Prices			not available			
Supply and use			Imports/exports of ornamentals available in "Basic Horticultural Statistics"			

source: Defra website, www.defra.gov.uk/esg

(a) Areas relate to field areas multiplied by the number of crops in the year and hence differ from those shown in table 3.2.

(b) Including forced flower bulbs.

Livestock

Gross indigenous production
(Tables 5.13, 5.14 and 5.15)

21   Two measures of production are shown in these tables. Gross Indigenous Production (GIP) is a measure of animal production commonly used in other EU states and is therefore useful for making international comparisons. It is measured as total slaughterings plus all live exports minus all live imports of breeding and non-breeding livestock. Home-fed Production includes imports and exports of non-breeding animals only, i.e. it is measured as total slaughterings plus live exports (non-breeding) minus live imports (non-breeding).

Cattle and calves: beef and veal
(Table 5.13)

22   The value of production of cattle and calves rose by 14 per cent in 2002 to £2.0 billion, due primarily to a 12 per cent increase in the value of home-fed production of beef and veal and a 13 per cent increase in direct subsidy and other payments to beef producers.

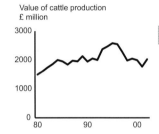

Value of cattle production
£ million

23   Clean cattle market prices have been stable, aided by a stronger trade, and a little above 2000 prices for most of the year. Livestock markets were closed for most of 2001 due to the outbreak of Foot and Mouth Disease so an average market price is not available for that year. Average deadweight prices (not shown in table 5.13) for 2002 were a little above those for 2001. The increase in direct subsidy and other payments was mainly due to increases in receipts arising from the Over Thirty Month Scheme (OTMS) which was closed for five months during 2001, and the Slaughter Premium Scheme as marketings recovered following the outbreak of Foot and Mouth Disease in 2001.

24   Clean cattle marketings rose by 7.4 per cent in 2002 reflecting a recovery following the outbreak of Foot and Mouth Disease in 2001. Home-fed production of beef and veal rose similarly by 7.2 per cent to 692 thousand tonnes while the amount of beef available for domestic use rose by 6.4 per cent to 959 thousand tonnes.

25   Measures of marketings, production and value exclude all cattle removed from the food chain by the OTMS, the Selective Cull and the Calf Processing Aid Scheme (CPAS, which ran from 22 April 1996 until 31 July 1999). These schemes were introduced following the beef crisis in March 1996. Payments to producers for the OTMS and CPAS are included as subsidies in the value of production. Payments under the Selective Cull are not included as the payments are for the replacement of capital assets.

26   Cattle slaughtered due to Foot and Mouth Disease in 2001 (including the preventative operations intended to circumscribe the outbreaks) and under the Livestock Welfare Disposal Scheme are also not included in marketings, production and value as these animals were removed from the food chain. Also, Foot and Mouth Disease compensation payments are not included in the value of production as these have been treated as payments for the loss of capital assets.

Sheep and lambs: mutton and lamb
(Table 5.14)

27   The value of production of sheep and lambs rose by 34 per cent to £840 million in 2002, owing to a 42 per cent increase in the value of home-fed production and a 31 per cent increase in subsidy payments.

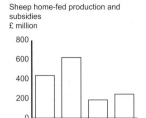

Sheep home-fed production and subsidies
£ million

28 A healthy demand for sheepmeat and a tightening of supply following the outbreak of Foot and Mouth Disease in 2001 saw lamb prices remain above 2000 levels throughout the year. Livestock markets were closed for most of 2001 due to the outbreak of Foot and Mouth Disease so an average market price is not available for that year. The increase in subsidy payments followed low payment rates in 2001 due to high average EU market prices in that year and a change from variable to fixed rate payments.

29 Clean sheep marketings rose by 17 per cent in 2002 due primarily to a recovery following the outbreak of Foot and Mouth Disease in 2001, but were 21 per cent below 2000, reflecting a fall in the breeding flock. Sheepmeat production rose by 15 per cent, to 306 thousand tonnes but was well below that in 2000. The amount of sheepmeat available for domestic use rose by 5.7 per cent to 361 thousand tonnes. Exports recovered a little during the year but were still only about half those in 2000.

30 In December 2001, changes to the way subsidies are paid to sheep farmers were adopted. These reforms, which came into effect from 1 January 2002, brought in fixed rate premiums and national envelopes. In 2002, £2.0 million of the Sheep National Envelope was used to fund a Sheep Quota Purchase Scheme (SQPS) with the purpose of reducing sheep numbers in areas that have faced historic overgrazing or on land that is of high biodiversity value, while the remainder was used to top up SAPS payments. Payments under the SQPS are not included in the value of subsidy payments as these have been treated as payments for the replacement of capital assets.

31 Sheep slaughtered due to Foot and Mouth Disease in 2001 (including the preventative operations intended to circumscribe the outbreak) and under the Livestock Welfare Disposal Scheme are not included in marketings, production and value as these animals were removed from the food chain. Also, Foot and Mouth Disease compensation payments are not included in the value of production as these have been treated as payments for the loss of capital assets. However, the 'light lambs' scheme, which operated in autumn 2001, has been included as direct support payments in the output value of production.

Pigs and pigmeat
(Table 5.15)

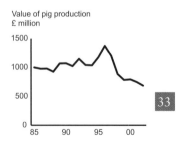

Value of pig production
£ million

32 The value of production of pigs fell by 8.3 per cent in 2002 to £687 million, half the peak value of £1.4 billion in 1996, due primarily to the value of home-fed production of pigmeat falling by 6.7 per cent to £688 million. A £15 million fall in work-in-progress (work-in-progress is the value of those pigs which are still in the process of being reared for slaughter) and a recovery in the export of breeding animals accounted for the balance.

33 Prices weakened in 2002, with the UK Adjusted Euro-Spec Average (AESA) easing from a little below 100 pence/kg at the beginning of 2002 to about 90 pence/kg in December, reflecting a downturn in world prices. Producers continued to leave the industry due to poor market returns, which is reflected in an 8.3% decline in the breeding herd to 483 thousand sows at June 2002.

34 Marketings of clean pigs fell by 4.5 per cent, primarily due to the continued contraction of the breeding herd, and average carcase weights continued to increase, averaging 72.3 kg, about 3 kg a pig more than in 1999. Marketings of sows and boars recovered after the export ban (put in place at the start of the outbreak of Foot and Mouth Disease) was lifted and the main market for sow meat reopened. Home-fed production of pigmeat fell slightly by 0.4 per cent to 774 thousand tonnes. An increase in the use of pigmeat for pork masked a fall in the use of pigmeat for bacon and ham.

35 Home-fed production of pork rose by 2.8 per cent to 628 thousand tonnes while the amount of pork available for domestic use fell by 0.6 per cent to 833 thousand tonnes, as a recovery in exports following the outbreak of Foot and Mouth Disease in 2001 more than offset a rise in imports. Exports, however, are at their lowest since 1990 (excepting 2001) while imports are the highest ever recorded at 295 thousand tonnes.

36 In 2002 home-cured production of bacon fell by 6.1 per cent to 185 thousand tonnes and the amount available for domestic use fell by 2.2 per cent to 460 thousand tonnes. As a result, imports now contribute over 60% of the domestic supplies of bacon and ham.

37 Pigs slaughtered due to Foot and Mouth Disease (including the preventative operations intended to circumscribe the outbreak) or Classical Swine Fever and under the Livestock Welfare Disposal Schemes are not included in marketings, production and value as these animals were removed from the food chain. Also, Foot and Mouth Disease compensation payments are not included in the value of production as these have been treated as payments for the loss of capital assets.

Poultry and poultrymeat
(Table 5.16)

38 Production of poultrymeat fell by 2.0 per cent in 2002 to 1.5 million tonnes with total slaughterings falling by 1.7 per cent. The value of production fell by £105 million (7.9 per cent) to £1.2 billion. Average producer poultrymeat prices fell during 2002: turkey meat fell by 6.4 per cent to 114.2 pence/kg and broiler meat fell by 3.4 per cent to 67.7 pence/kg. However, the average producer price for geese rose by 59 per cent to 433.1 pence/kg. Imports rose by 7.4 thousand tonnes (2.1 per cent) and exports rose by 7.2 thousand tonnes (3.9 per cent).

Poultry production
'000 tonnes

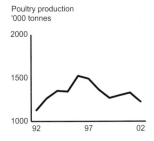

Table 5.13 Cattle and calves: beef and veal

Inquiries: Steve Walton on 01904 455090 email: steve.walton@defra.gsi.gov.uk

	Average of 1991-1993	1998 (a)	1999	2000	2001	2002 (provisional)
Population						
Total cattle and calves ('000 head at June)	11 926	11 519	11 423	11 133	10 600	10 343
of which: dairy cows	2 707	2 439	2 440	2 336	2 251	2 227
beef cows	1 739	1 947	1 924	1 842	1 708	1 656
dairy heifers in-calf	550	563	549	532	502	470
beef heifers in-calf	219	225	214	186	199	257
other	6 711	6 345	6 296	6 238	5 940	5 732
Production (b)						
Total home-fed marketings ('000 head)	3 750	2 314	2 296	2 422	2 146	2 306
of which: steers, heifers and young bulls	2 614	2 278	2 216	2 265	2 049	2 197
calves	458	32	75	153	92	105
cows and adult bulls	678	4	4	4	5	3
Average dressed carcase weights (dcw) (kg) (c):						
steers, heifers and young bulls	289.2	306.4	304.6	308.9	313.2	315.0
calves	67.7	35.3	31.6	27.5	27.5	27.2
cows and adult bulls	284.2	251.1	273.6	249.2	254.1	248.9
Production ('000 tonnes, dcw):						
home-fed production	963	699	679	706	645	692
gross indigenous production	954	698	676	702	638	687
Value of production (£ million)	2 141	1 982	2 047	1 994	1 772	2 024
of which: value of home-fed production	1 934	1 055	1 093	1 114	998	1 117
subsidies (d)	259	923	901	899	815	923
change in work-in-progress (e)	- 29	6	54	- 18	- 39	- 14
less imported livestock	25	3	2	2	2	1
plus breeding animals exported	2	..	..	..	..	..
Prices						
Store cattle (£ per head) (f):						
1st quality Hereford/cross bull calves (g)	150.4	107.9	88.2	79.5	..	85.2
1st quality beef/cross yearling steers (h)	431.6	369.0	382.0	400.0	..	398.1
Finished cattle (pence per kg liveweight): All clean cattle	114.8	86.1	92.1	89.8	..	91.4
Over Thirty Month, Selective Cull and Calf Processing Aid Schemes (i)						
Over Thirty Month Scheme:						
clean cattle throughput ('000 head)	..	71	72	62	55	65
cull cattle throughput ('000 head)	..	826	898	910	562	766
receipts (£ million)	..	239	266	260	157	205
Selective Cull scheme:						
throughput ('000 head)	..	19	-	-	-	-
receipts (£ million)	..	43	-	-	-	-
Calf Processing Aid Scheme:						
throughput ('000 head)	..	671	307	..	..	..
receipts (£ million)	..	52	20	..	..	..

Calendar years

continued

Table 5.13 continued

	Average of 1991-1993	1998 (a)	1999	2000	2001	2002 (provisional)
Supply and use ('000 tonnes, dcw) (j)						
Home-fed production (b)	963	699	679	706	645	692
Imports from: the EU (k) (l)	161	92	125	133	189	190
the rest of the world	45	60	59	64	74	89
Exports to: the EU (l)	144	9	10	9	8	11
the rest of the world	34	-	-	-	-	-
Total new supply	991	842	852	894	900	960
Increase in stocks	21	- 16	- 83	- 21	- 1	2
Total domestic uses	970	858	934	915	901	959
Home-fed production as % of total new supply for use in UK	97%	83%	80%	79%	72%	72%
Closing stocks	221	144	61	40	39	40

source: Defra website, www.defra.gov.uk/esg

(a) For comparability with other years, the figures have been adjusted from a 53-week to a 52-week basis where appropriate.

(b) Excludes cattle slaughtered under the Over Thirty Month Scheme and Selective Cull and calves slaughtered under the Calf Processing Aid Scheme. Also excludes cattle slaughtered under Foot and Mouth Disease control measures and Livestock Welfare Disposal Scheme.

(c) Average dressed carcase weight of animals fed and slaughtered in the UK.

(d) Comprising variable premium, calf subsidy, hill livestock compensatory allowances, suckler cow premium, beef special premium, deseasonalisation premium, extensification payments and slaughter premium. Includes payments made under the Over Thirty Month Scheme and the Calf Processing Aid Scheme.

(e) A valuation of the change in work-in-progress of animals to be slaughtered.

(f) Average prices at representative markets in England and Wales.

(g) Category changes: Prior to January 1988, 1st quality Hereford/Friesian bull calves. From January 1988, 1st quality Hereford/cross bull calves. From January 2002, Hereford/cross bull calves.

(h) Category changes: Prior to January 1988, 1st quality yearling steers beef/dairy cross. From January 1988, Hereford/cross, Charolais/cross, Limousin/cross, Simmental/cross, Belgian blue/cross, other continental/cross, other beef/dairy cross, other beef/beef cross. From January 2002, Hereford/cross, Continental/cross, others.

(i) Cattle slaughtered under these schemes are not included within the volume of production. Receipts for the Over Thirty Month Scheme and the Calf Processing Aid Scheme are included as subsidies. Selective Cull payments are not included in the income account.

(j) Does not include meat offals or trade in preserved or manufactured meat products. Boneless meat has been converted to bone-in weights.

(k) Includes meat from finished animals imported from the Irish Republic.

(l) All trade figures include an estimate for unrecorded trade.

Table 5.14 Sheep and lambs: mutton and lamb

Inquiries: Steve Walton on 01904 455090 email: steve.walton@defra.gsi.gov.uk

Calendar years

	Average of 1991-1993	1998 (a)	1999	2000	2001	2002 (provisional)
Population						
Total sheep and lambs ('000 head at June)	44 381	44 471	44 656	42 261	36 697	35 832
of which: breeding flock	20 760	21 260	21 458	20 447	17 911	17 628
lambs under 1 year old	22 405	22 138	22 092	20 855	17 759	17 309
others	1 216	1 073	1 106	959	1 027	896
Production (b)						
Total home-fed marketings ('000 head)	21 781	19 696	20 801	19 574	13 242	15 357
of which: clean sheep and lambs	19 687	17 711	18 499	17 129	11 475	13 454
ewes and rams	2 094	1 985	2 302	2 445	1 767	1 903
Average dressed carcase weights (dcw) (kg) (c):						
clean sheep and lambs	17.7	17.8	17.6	18.2	18.7	18.7
ewes and rams	27.5	29.7	28.3	28.5	28.2	29.2
Production ('000 tonnes, dcw):						
home-fed production	408	375	392	382	266	306
gross indigenous production	408	375	392	381	265	306
Value of production (£ million)	1 166	1 112	984	953	625	840
of which: value of home-fed production	642	626	595	637	439	622
subsidies (d)	539	479	410	337	189	248
change in work-in-progress (e)	- 11	11	- 15	- 15	- 2	- 31
less imported livestock	4	4	5	7	1	-
plus breeding animals exported	-	-	-	-	-	-
Prices						
Store sheep (£ per head) (f):						
lambs, hoggets and tegs	36.3	31.3	28.6	34.5	. .	33.1
Finished sheep (pence per kg estimated dcw) (g):						
Great Britain	183.1	192.5	180.3	196.4	. .	233.4
Northern Ireland	183.8	179.1	165.7	182.7	. .	222.8
Supply and use ('000 tonnes, dcw) (h)						
Home-fed production (b)	408	375	392	382	266	306
Imports from: the EU (i) (j)	6	18	17	17	15	13
the rest of the world	121	124	121	117	98	108
Exports to: the EU (j)	148	135	142	124	38	65
the rest of the world	2	1	1	1	-	-
Total new supply	384	380	386	391	341	363
Change in stocks	- 2	-	- 1	- 5	- 1	2
Total domestic uses	386	381	387	395	342	361
Home-fed production as % of total new supply for use in UK	107%	101%	104%	100%	78%	84%
Closing stocks	16	15	14	9	8	10

source: Defra website, www.defra.gov.uk/esg

continued

Table 5.14 continued

(a) For comparability with other years, the figures have been adjusted from a 53-week to a 52-week basis where appropriate.

(b) Excludes sheep and lambs slaughtered under Foot and Mouth Disease control measures and Livestock Welfare Disposal Scheme (including 'light lambs' scheme).

(c) Average dressed carcase weight of animals fed and slaughtered in the UK.

(d) Comprising variable premium, hill livestock compensatory allowances, sheep annual premium and 'light lambs' Welfare Disposal Scheme.

(e) A valuation of the change in work-in-progress of animals to be slaughtered.

(f) Average prices at representative markets in England and Wales, excluding prices at autumn hill sheep sales. Category changes: Prior to January 2002, 1st quality lambs, hoggets and tegs. From January 2002, lambs, hoggets and tegs.

(g) Unweighted average of weekly prices at representative markets as reported to the European Commission.

(h) Does not include meat offals or trade in preserved or manufactured meat products. Boneless meat has been converted to bone-in weights.

(i) Includes meat from finished animals imported from the Irish Republic.

(j) All trade figures include an estimate for unrecorded trade.

Table 5.15 Pigs and pigmeat

Inquiries: Steve Walton on 01904 455090 email: steve.walton@defra.gsi.gov.uk.

Calendar years

	Average of 1991-1993	1998 (a)	1999	2000	2001	2002 (provisional)
Population						
Total pigs ('000 head at June)	7 751	8 146	7 284	6 482	5 845	5 588
of which: sows in pig and other sows for breeding	690	675	603	537	527	483
gilts in pig	112	103	85	73	71	74
other	6 949	7 368	6 595	5 872	5 247	5 030
Production (b)						
Total home-fed marketings ('000 head)	14 885	16 058	14 691	12 377	10 571	10 235
of which: clean pigs	14 507	15 640	14 312	12 054	10 386	9 916
sows and boars	378	418	378	322	184	319
Average dressed carcase weights (dcw) (kg) (c):						
clean pigs	66.0	69.1	69.1	70.7	72.1	72.3
sows and boars	143.3	142.3	145.3	148.4	156.0	155.2
Production ('000 tonnes, dcw):						
home-fed production	1 011	1 135	1 042	899	777	774
gross indigenous production	1 010	1 135	1 043	900	777	767
Value of production (£ million)	1 072	887	785	794	749	687
of which: value of home-fed production	1 059	889	792	821	738	688
change in work-in-progress (d)	5	- 8	- 11	- 31	11	- 4
less imported livestock	-	-	-	-	-	-
plus breeding animals exported	7	5	4	4	-	2
Prices						
Clean pigs (pence per kg deadweight)	106.9	80.6	78.6	94.4	97.8	93.5
Supply and use of pork ('000 tonnes, dcw) (e) (f)						
Home-fed production (b)	809	931	831	725	610	628
Imports from: the EU (g) (h)	93	187	231	269	259	293
the rest of the world	1	3	3	5	2	2
Exports to: the EU (h)	121	258	201	175	35	86
the rest of the world	3	35	34	33	4	6
Total new supply	778	829	831	790	832	830
Change in stocks	-	2	- 3	- 7	4	- 3
Total domestic uses	778	827	834	798	828	833
Home-fed production as % of total new supply for use in UK	104%	112%	100%	92%	73%	76%
Closing stocks	11	18	15	8	12	8
Supply and use of bacon and ham						
('000 tonnes, product weight) (e)						
Home-cured production	199	236	233	209	197	185
Imports from: the EU	242	231	230	268	281	284
the rest of the world	-	-	-	-	-	-
Exports to: the EU	4	8	6	9	7	10
the rest of the world	-	-	-	-	-	-
Total new supply	437	459	457	468	471	459
Increase in stocks	- 1	- 1	2	- 1	1	- 1
Total domestic uses	438	460	455	468	470	460
Home-cured production as % of total new supply for use in UK	46%	51%	51%	45%	42%	40%
Closing stocks	3	3	5	4	5	4

source: Defra website, www.defra.gov.uk/esg

continued

Table 5.15 continued

(a) For comparability with other years, the figures have been adjusted from a 53-week to a 52-week basis where appropriate.

(b) Excludes pigs slaughtered under Foot and Mouth Disease and swine fever control measures and welfare disposal schemes.

(c) Average dressed carcase weight of animals fed and slaughtered in the UK.

(d) A valuation of the change in work-in-progress of animals to be slaughtered.

(e) Does not include meat offals or trade in preserved or manufactured meat products.

(f) Boneless meat has been converted to bone-in weights.

(g) Includes meat from finished animals imported from the Irish Republic.

(h) All trade figures include an estimate for unrecorded trade.

2002

Table 5.16   Poultry and poultrymeat

Inquiries: Michael Chatten on 01904 455092 email: michael.j.chatten@defra.gsi.gov.uk

		Average of 1991-1993	1998 (a)	1999	2000	2001	Calendar years 2002 (provisional)
Production							
Number ('000 head at June) (b):		119 451	152 906	153 621	157 051	166 896	155 745
of which:	chickens and other table fowls	76 600	98 244	101 625	105 688	112 531	105 137
	birds in the laying flock (c)	33 243	29 483	29 258	28 686	29 895	28 778
	fowls for breeding	7 244	10 023	9 401	10 667	12 083	10 724
	turkeys, ducks and geese (d)	2 365	15 157	13 337	12 010	12 387	11 107
Slaughterings (millions) (e):		706	856	848	843	866	851
of which:	fowls	659	804	800	797	818	808
	turkeys	34	34	29	27	26	23
	ducks	12	18	18	18	21	20
	geese	1	1	1	1	1	-
Production ('000 tonnes carcase weight) (f):		1 232	1 546	1 525	1 513	1 565	1 533
of which:	chickens and other table fowls	921	1 153	1 161	1 164	1 213	1 205
	boiling fowls (culled hens)	47	56	53	51	49	50
	turkeys	234	294	267	255	254	232
	ducks	28	40	41	40	47	44
	geese	3	3	3	3	2	2
Value of production (£ million):		1 160	1 367	1 272	1 303	1 332	1 227
of which:	fowls	789	892	839	830	855	821
	change in work-in-progress in fowls	3	- 11	- 21	2	14	- 21
	turkeys, ducks, geese	328	430	397	408	395	348
	exports of live poultry	33	45	50	60	62	67
	hatching eggs for export	12	19	15	13	17	22
	less live poultry imported	4	5	5	5	5	4
	less hatching eggs imported	1	3	4	5	5	6
Prices (Average producer price (pence/kg carcase weight))							
for:	chickens and other table fowls	113.2	76.8	71.8	70.8	70.1	67.7
	boiling fowls (culled hens)	35.7	11.5	10.3	10.7	9.8	10.0
	turkeys	121.7	122.3	118.8	129.6	122.1	114.2
	ducks	128.3	161.9	173.9	170.3	165.7	166.6
	geese	178.0	206.0	307.1	319.1	272.9	433.1
Supply and use of poultrymeat							
('000 tonnes carcase weight) (e)							
Production		1 232	1 546	1 525	1 513	1 565	1 533
Imports from:	the EU	166	293	318	321	302	309
	the rest of the world	-	23	31	34	44	45
Exports to:	the EU	65	128	110	116	140	146
	the rest of the world	19	69	76	58	46	48
Total new supply		1 313	1 664	1 687	1 694	1 724	1 693
Change in stocks		2	15	- 9	- 13	8	8
Total domestic uses		1 312	1 649	1 696	1 707	1 716	1 685
Production as % of total new supply		94%	93%	90%	89%	91%	91%

source: Defra website, www.defra.gov.uk/esg

continued

Table 5.16 continued

(a) For comparability with other years, the figures have been adjusted from a 53 week to a 52 week basis where appropriate.

(b) From 1998 the collection of data for England and Wales was simplified. Figures for 1998 onwards are not directly comparable with years prior to 1998.

(c) Hens and pullets kept mainly for producing eggs for eating.

(d) Data prior to 1996 does not include figures for turkeys.

(e) Slaughtering figures include registered and unregistered slaughterhouses.

(f) Excludes offal.

2002

Livestock products

Milk and milk products
(Tables 5.17 and 5.18)

39 The value of production of milk produced for human consumption fell by 12 per cent to £2.5 billion. This was primarily due to a £260 million fall in the value of milk sold for processing by dairy companies, which in turn arose mainly from a 2.13 pence per litre fall in the average milk price received by farmers in 2002.

40 There was a £6.6 million increase in the value of milk products (such as cheese and butter) produced on farm for sale direct to consumers arising from increased producer prices for these items. No further agrimonetary compensation payments were payable and no superlevy charge arose as milk production in the 2001/02 quota year did not exceed quota for the second year in a row.

41 High winter milk production followed by plentiful grass growth produced a very large spring flush of milk. This, and weak commodity markets, saw prices decline at the beginning of the year and then fall sharply in April by 2.02 pence per litre. Agreements by supermarkets to raise prices for milk, cheese and other milk products helped farm gate prices to move ahead in October, but the average price for the year fell by 11 per cent to 17.13 pence per litre, marginally higher than two years ago.

42 Butter prices on European markets remained low for most of 2002 although there was a slight improvement towards the end of the year. Intervention therefore figured largely, being open in between eight and twelve Member States including the UK, between the months of January and August. A further measure to help stabilise butter prices was private storage aid (PSA) for butter being brought forward by two weeks to open at the beginning of March. As world butter prices were also low, export refunds for butter were increased between January and July 2002. Between the end of August and December the number of Member States with intervention open generally decreased from ten to six (intervention in the UK was open throughout) as the world and the EU price of butter began to increase slightly. Sizeable amounts of butter were sold into store over 2002 and EU intervention stocks of butter reached 191 thousand tonnes in December (of which 15 thousand tonnes in the UK).

43 World prices for skimmed milk powder (SMP) and whole milk powder (WMP) remained low for the majority of 2002 making EU prices uncompetitive. As a result, export refunds for these products were increased between January and July. EU prices also remained low throughout this period and, when intervention for SMP opened at the beginning of March, 145 thousand tonnes were intervened before it closed at the end of August. In a further measure to strengthen the market, the minimum incorporation rate for subsidised SMP used in animal feed reverted to 50 per cent on 1st January 2002, increasing uptake. Between September and December the world market for SMP and WMP began to improve and prices rose. Export refunds were therefore cut from September onwards. As a result of the improved prices nearly 10 thousand tonnes of EU SMP intervention stocks were sold over November and December for animal feed or for other uses.

Hen Eggs 44
(Table 5.19)

Egg production
million eggs

44 Overall value of production of eggs for human consumption increased by £70 million (17 per cent) to £476 million. The total quantity of egg production for human consumption rose by 48 million dozen (5.9 per cent) to 854 million dozen. Within this, processed eggs rose by 1.7 per cent whilst eggs sold in shell, which accounted for 84 per cent of the eggs sold for human consumption in 2002, rose by 6.8 per cent. The average egg price rose by 2.3 per cent to 55.7 pence per dozen.

Table 5.17 Milk

Inquiries: Colin Beattie on 01904 455095 email: colin.j.beattie@defra.gsi.gov.uk

Million litres (unless otherwise specified)   Calendar years

	Average of 1991-1993	1998	1999	2000 (a)	2001	2002 (provisional)
Population and yield						
Dairy herd (annual average, '000 head) (b)	2 745	2 461	2 445	2 354	2 251	2 219
Average yield per dairy cow (litres per annum)	5 211	5 774	5 964	5 977	6 347	6 531
Production						
Production of milk from the dairy herd (c)	14 301	14 210	14 581	14 071	14 285	14 488
Production of milk from the beef herd (c)	7	7	7	7	7	7
less on farm waste and milk fed to stock	276	280	285	277	283	282
Volume for human consumption	14 033	13 937	14 303	13 801	14 009	14 213
Value of production (£ million)	2 967	2 709	2 653	2 393	2 822	2 489
of which: milk (d)	2 896	2 656	2 586	2 300	2 658	2 397
milk products (e)	102	84	76	86	85	92
agrimonetary compensation	..	..	..	22	79	..
less levies (f)	31	32	9	15	..	..
Prices (pence per litre) (g)						
Farmgate price of milk excluding bonus payments	..	19.26	18.30	16.91	19.14	17.04
Farmgate price of milk including bonus payments	..	19.37	18.35	16.93	19.26	17.13
Supply and use (h)						
Production	14 308	14 217	14 588	14 078	14 292	14 523
Imports	..	129	111	105	64	74
Exports	75	373	465	445	414	427
Total domestic use	14 233	13 973	14 234	13 737	13 942	14 170
of which:						
for liquid consumption	6 763	6 739	6 853	6 768	6 761	6 829
for manufacture	7 042	6 821	6 988	6 550	6 715	6 874
of which						
butter (i)	269	281	290	270	259	289
cheese	3 272	3 257	3 297	3 032	3 568	3 576
cream (i)	265	263	271	266	259	253
condensed milk (j)	723	643	603	522	536	504
milk powder - full cream	532	809	853	932	781	776
milk powder - skimmed	1 429	1 101	1 123	889	663	794
other	551	467	549	640	649	682
Dairy wastage and stock change	..	80	56	91	132	105
Other uses (k)	..	333	338	328	335	361

source: Defra website, www.defra.gov.uk/esg

(a) 366 days.

(b) Dairy herd is defined as cows and heifers in milk plus cows in calf but not in milk, kept mainly for producing milk or rearing calves for the dairy herd.

(c) Excludes suckled milk.

(d) Value of milk sold for processing off farm. Excludes milk processed on farm and sold direct to the consumer.

(e) Value of milk products manufactured on farm for sale direct to the consumer.

(f) Comprising milk co-responsibility levy from 1977 to 1993 and milk superlevy.

(g) The farmgate price is the average price received by milk producers, net of delivery charges. No deduction is made for superlevy. In the current year, estimated bonuses for April to December have been included.

(h) Aggregated data from surveys run by Defra, SEERAD and DARD, NI on the utilisation of milk by dairies.

(i) Includes the utilisation of the residual fat of low fat liquid milk production.

(j) Includes condensed milk used in the production of chocolate crumb and in the production of machine skimmed milk.

(k) Includes farmhouse consumption, milk fed to stock and on farm waste. Excludes suckled milk.

Table 5.18   Milk products

Inquiries: Colin Beattie on 01904 455095 email: colin.j.beattie@defra.gsi.gov.uk

This data shows UK production and supplies of milk products manufactured by both dairy companies and on farm. The data is quoted in thousand tonnes and is not directly comparable with the data shown in table 5.17 which is quoted in million litres.

Thousand tonnes (unless otherwise specified)   Calendar years

		Average of 1991-1993	1998	1999	2000	2001	2002 (provisional)
Butter (a) (b)							
Production (c)		134	137	141	132	126	141
Imports from:	the EU	59	57	67	80	76	62
	the rest of the world	55	48	47	38	39	39
Exports to:	the EU (d)	42	50	50	39	36	33
	the rest of the world	5	15	6	6	5	4
Total new supply (d)		200	176	199	204	201	204
Change in stocks (e)		- 13	4	11	- 5	1	8
Total domestic uses (d) (e)		213	172	187	209	200	196
Production as % of total new supply for use in UK		67%	78%	71%	64%	63%	69%
Closing stocks (e)		54	11	22	17	18	26
Cheese							
Production (c)		326	366	368	340	395	6
Imports from:	the EU	187	225	236	225	246	241
	the rest of the world	18	32	41	30	29	26
Exports to:	the EU	30	45	49	48	57	57
	the rest of the world	22	10	13	10	11	20
Total new supply		479	567	584	536	601	586
Change in stocks		-	- 10	1	-	5	2
Total domestic uses		479	577	583	536	596	584
Production as % of total new supply for use in UK		68%	64%	63%	63%	66%	68%
Closing stocks (f)		24	9	10	10	15	17
Cream - fresh, frozen, sterilized							
Production (b) (c)		250	266	275	270	263	257
Imports from:	the EU	3	11	8	10	18	12
	the rest of the world	-	-	-	-	-	-
Exports to:	the EU	47	100	95	81	83	95
	the rest of the world	2	1	1	1	1	-
Total new supply		203	176	188	198	197	174
Change in stocks		. .	. .	. .	. .	. .	. .
Total domestic uses		203	176	188	198	197	174
Production as % of total new supply for use in UK		123%	151%	146%	137%	134%	148%
Closing stocks		. .	. .	. .	. .	. .	. .

continued

Table 5.18 continued

Thousand tonnes (unless otherwise specified)   Calendar years

		Average of 1991-1993	1998	1999	2000	2001	2002 (provisional)
Condensed milk (g)							
Production		198	192	177	162	161	149
Imports from:	the EU	11	13	14	15	14	11
	the rest of the world	-	-	-	-	-	-
Exports to:	the EU	9	43	38	28	20	28
	the rest of the world	43	21	13	3	2	2
Total new supply		158	141	139	145	153	131
Change in stocks		- 1	- 1	1	- 1	3	- 1
Total domestic uses		159	141	138	146	150	131
Production as % of total new supply for use in UK		126%	136%	127%	111%	105%	114%
Closing stocks		10	7	8	7	10	9
Milk powder - full cream							
Production		78	97	102	105	83	105
Imports from:	the EU	5	10	10	11	8	10
	the rest of the world	-	0	0	0	0	0
Exports to:	the EU	25	26	28	28	29	53
	the rest of the world	45	80	64	74	57	60
Total new supply		13	1	20	14	5	1
Change in stocks		-	-	-	- 1	3	- 2
Total domestic uses		13	1	20	15	2	3
Closing stocks		3	3	3	2	5	3
Skimmed milk powder							
Production		127	107	102	83	71	71
Imports from:	the EU	16	11	14	13	23	14
	the rest of the world	-	-	-	-	-	-
Exports to:	the EU (d)	44	21	30	77	26	17
	the rest of the world	13	13	30	35	4	6
Total new supply (d)		85	85	57	- 16	63	61
Change in stocks		- 3	27	- 11	- 66	7	16
Total domestic uses (d)		88	57	68	50	56	45
Production as % of total new supply for use in UK		149%	127%	180%	- 527%	111%	117%
Closing stocks		14	82	71	5	12	29

source: Defra website, www.defra.gov.uk/esg

(a) Includes butterfat and oil, dehydrated butter and ghee.

(b) Includes production from the residual fat of low fat milk products.

(c) Includes farmhouse manufacture.

(d) These figures include the use of these products for animal feed.

(e) In addition to stocks in public cold stores surveyed by Defra, closing stocks include all intervention stocks in private cold stores. Total domestic uses does not equate exactly with consumption since changes in unrecorded stocks are not included in the calculation.

(f) Cheese stocks held in public cold stores. Public cold stores make their storage space available to the public or to the Rural Payments Agency, formerly the Intervention Board. The ownership of the store, whether public or private, is irrelevant.

(g) Includes condensed milk used in the production of chocolate crumb and in the production of sweetened and unsweetened machine skimmed milk.

Table 5.19   Hen eggs

Inquiries: Michael Chatten on 01904 455092 email: michael.j.chatten@defra.gsi.gov.uk

Calendar years

	Average of 1991-1993	1998 (a)	1999	2000	2001	2002 (provisional)
Production						
Volume of production of eggs (million dozen)	894	902	850	855	917	967
of which: eggs for human consumption	805	792	743	747	806	854
eggs for hatching (b)	77	94	93	94	95	94
hatching eggs for export (c)	3	7	5	5	6	9
waste	9	9	8	9	9	10
Production for human consumption:						
Number of fowls laying eggs for eating (millions) (d)	35.7	32.9	30.7	30.8	33.4	35.4
Average yield per layer (number of eggs per bird per year)	271	289	290	291	290	290
Value of production of eggs for human consumption (£ million) (e)	403	381	344	371	406	476
Prices (pence per dozen)						
Average price	50.1	51.5	49.7	53.1	54.5	55.7
UK graded egg price weighted average (f)	38.2	36.3	34.2	36.4	37.8	38.5
Supply and use (million dozen)						
UK production of eggs for human consumption	805	792	743	747	806	854
of which: eggs sold in shell	715	662	605	610	671	716
eggs processed	90	130	139	136	136	138
Imports from (g): the EU	46	63	68	91	113	133
the rest of the world	1	1	2	3	4	9
Exports to (g): the EU	15	30	15	15	8	12
the rest of the world	1	7	3	3	3	3
Total new supply	835	819	795	822	912	982
Production of eggs for human consumption as % of total new supply for use in UK	96%	97%	93%	91%	88%	87%

source: Defra website, www.defra.gov.uk/esg

(a) For comparability with other years, the figures for 1998 have been adjusted from a 53 week to a 52 week basis.

(b) Eggs for hatching are not valued as they are included in the final value of poultry.

(c) Hatching eggs for export are valued in table 5.16.

(d) Population is implied from gross production and average yield and hence differs from the census figures in table 3.2.

(e) Excludes value of eggs for hatching.

(f) Represents the UK Packer to Producer Price excluding bonus. Takes account of all egg systems - laying cages, free range, barn.

(g) Includes shell egg equivalent of whole (dried, frozen and liquid) egg, egg yolk and albumen.

Purchased feedingstuffs and seeds

Purchased feedingstuffs
(Table 5.20)

45 The total cost of all purchased feedingstuffs fell by £148 million, or 6.4 per cent, to £2.2 billion in 2002. This was due to a decline in feed volumes in both the compound feed (except for poultry) and straight feed sectors. However, rather than indicating any significant movement within the feed patterns of the industry itself in areas outside the poultry sector, it is more likely to be as a result of the exceptional circumstances caused by Foot and Mouth Disease in 2001.

46 The 6.0 per cent increase in volume of compound feed for the poultry sector reflects a move away from feed production for own use within large poultry units (shown within the straight concentrates area of the table) into the manufacture of these compounds by retail compounders.

Purchased seeds
(Table 5.21)

47 The total cost and the volume of purchased seeds in 2002 remained very similar to 2001 at £295 million and 1.0 million tonnes respectively. There was a slight increase (3.7 per cent) in the volume of seed potatoes and a fall in the volume of seeds for root and fodder crops of 9.2 per cent.

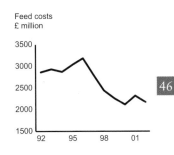

Feed costs £ million

Table 5.20 Feedingstuffs

Including direct inter-farm and intra-farm transfer

Inquiries: Alex Clothier on 01904 455068 email: alex.clothier@defra.gsi.gov.uk

Thousand tonnes (unless otherwise specified)   Calendar years

	Average of 1991-1993	1998	1999	2000	2001	2002 (provisional)
Compounds:						
cattle	4 081	3 732	4 176	3 940	4 260	4 028
calves	255	202	187	190	179	167
pigs	2 463	2 751	2 469	2 113	1 967	1 808
poultry (a)	3 104	3 129	3 181	3 057	3 251	3 445
other	612	725	874	736	704	613
Total (b)	10 550	10 412	10 750	9 891	10 214	9 959
Straight concentrates (i.e. cereals, cereal offals, proteins and other high energy feeds)	6 052	5 815	6 019	6 563	6 649	5 925
Non-concentrates (low-energy bulk feeds expressed as concentrate equivalent) (c)	555	527	526	525	525	525
Inter/intra farm transfer	3 153	3 490	3 151	2 850	2 921	3 071
Total all purchased feedingstuffs	19 982	20 243	20 446	19 828	20 309	19 479
Value of purchased feedingstuffs (£ million) (d)	2 889	2 444	2 261	2 117	2 323	2 175

source: Defra Statistics website, www.defra.gov.uk/esg

(a) This item includes poultry feed produced by 'retail' compounders, but excludes production from integrated poultry units which are included within the straight data.

(b) Including imports, less exports.

(c) Brewers and distillers grains, hay, milk by-products and other low-energy bulk feeds expressed in terms of equivalent tonnage of high energy feeds.

(d) See Table 6.1 for a breakdown of this total.

Table 5.21 Purchased seeds

Inquiries: Lindsay Holmes on 01904 455563 email: lindsay.holmes@defra.gsi.gov.uk

Thousand tonnes (unless otherwise specified)   Calendar years

	Average of 1991-1993	1998	1999	2000	2001	2002 (provisional)
Cereals (a)	459	387	433	391	422	415
Grass and clover	11	12	11	11	11	11
Root and fodder crops	47	44	44	46	61	55
Potatoes (b)	500	432	440	448	386	400
Vegetable and other horticultural seeds (c)	114	132	138	144	145	145
Total purchased seeds	1 131	1 007	1 066	1 041	1 025	1 027
Total value of all purchased seeds (£ million)	308	331	331	273	292	295

source: Defra website, www.defra.gov.uk/esg

(a) Restricted to the purchase of certified seed only.

(b) Includes farm-saved seed.

(c) Includes bulbs and seeds for hardy nursery stock, flowers, sugar beet and oilseed rape.

Chapter **6** Accounts

Total Income from Farming

1 Total Income from Farming in the UK in 2002 is estimated to have risen by 15 per cent (14 per cent in real terms) compared with its 2001 level. Total Income from Farming (TIFF) is income generated by production within the agriculture industry, including subsidies. It represents business profits plus remuneration for work done by owners and other unpaid workers. Although having risen in 2001 and 2002, TIFF is still 56 per cent below its peak in 1995 (62 per cent in real terms) after more than doubling between 1990 and 1995.

2 TIFF is sensitive to small percentage changes in the values of outputs and inputs. This sensitivity, the provisional nature of the figures for the latest year and revisions made to previously published figures for earlier years, as methodology or data sources improve, all need to be borne in mind when using these figures.

Treatment of foot and mouth losses

3 TIFF excludes payments for livestock destroyed for Foot and Mouth Disease control and associated welfare purposes in 2001. This is a consequence of the decision taken jointly by Defra, the Office for National Statistics and Eurostat based on internationally agreed standards.

4 Destroyed livestock are treated as "exceptional losses", as defined in the European System of Accounts 1995, and shown in the other changes in the volume of assets account. It follows from this decision that all payments for animals destroyed are treated as capital transfers and are not part of income. They are therefore shown in the capital account, table 6.4. In addition, it also follows that the part-production of livestock being reared for slaughter, that had already taken place up until the time of the cull, is included in the production account, and contributes to output and income. Destroyed breeding livestock do not contribute to output or income (although their depreciation up until the point of culling is allowed for).

Aggregate Agricultural Account
(Tables 6.1 and 6.2, Charts 6.1 and 6.2)

5 The Aggregate Agricultural Account provides details of the industry's outputs, inputs and generation of income. It conforms to internationally agreed accounting principles required by both UK national accounts and by Eurostat.

6 Table 6.1 shows the full production and income account at current prices with Chart 6.1 showing how the main aggregates in the account are related. Table 6.2 shows the value, price and volume changes between 2001 and 2002. Changes in value are shown in Chart 6.2.

7 These tables show estimates of:

(a) output at basic prices by product and total output at market prices after deducting subsidies;

(b) transactions that take place wholly within the agricultural industry;

Chart 6.1 Main components of the aggregate account (£ billion)

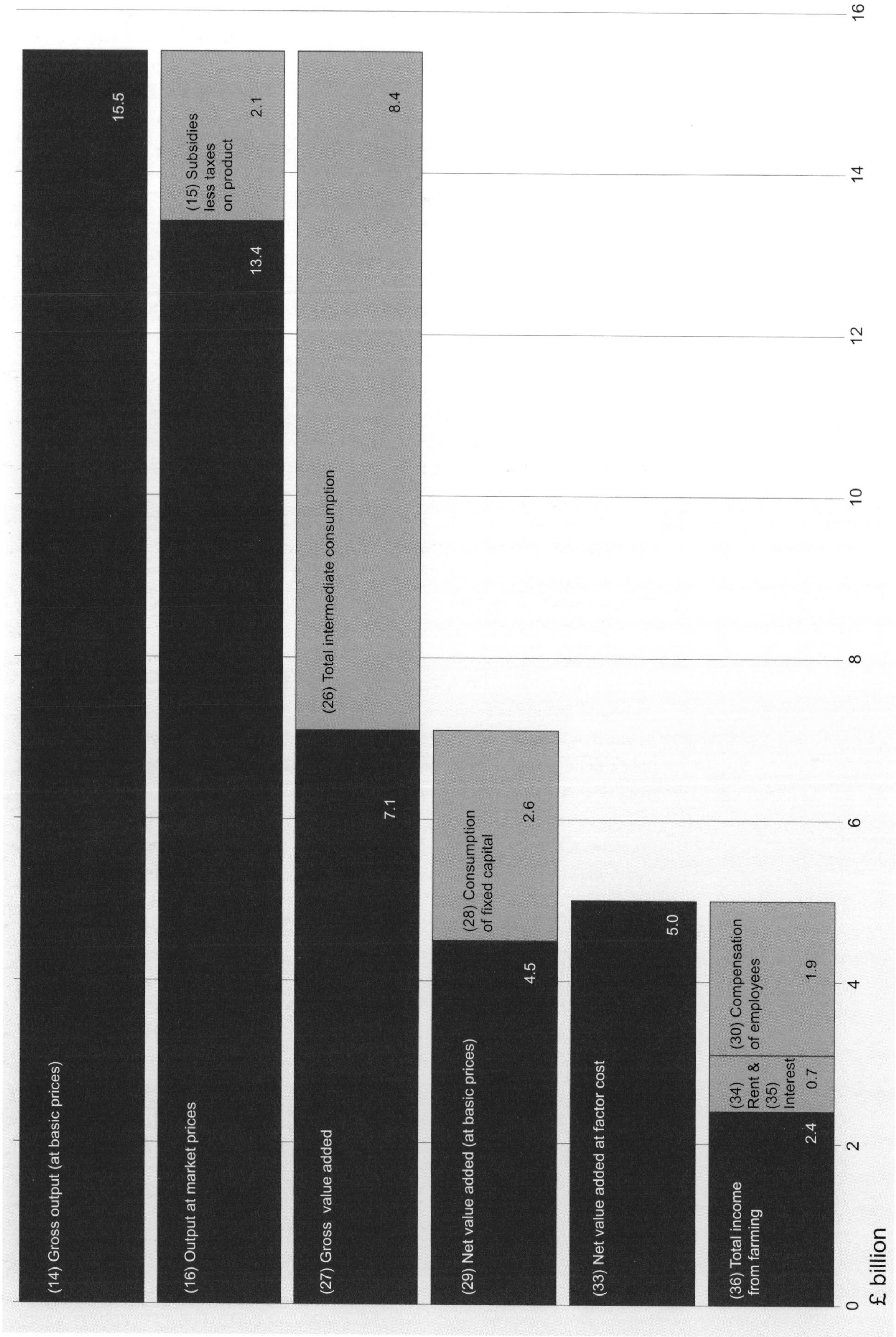

(14) Gross output (at basic prices) — 15.5

(16) Output at market prices — 13.4
(15) Subsidies less taxes on product — 2.1

(27) Gross value added — 7.1
(26) Total intermediate consumption — 8.4

(29) Net value added (at basic prices) — 4.5
(28) Consumption of fixed capital — 2.6

(33) Net value added at factor cost — 5.0

(36) Total income from farming — 2.4
(34) Rent & (35) Interest — 0.7
(30) Compensation of employees — 1.9

£ billion

0   2   4   6   8   10   12   14   16

(c) inputs - intermediate consumption, consumption of fixed capital (i.e. the reduction in value of capital assets due to depreciation), compensation of employees, rent and interest payments.

8 The value of output (including subsidies directly related to products) was slightly higher, up by 1.1 per cent in 2002. The volume was 4.8 per cent higher mainly due to increases in cereals and livestock. Prices received were 3.6 per cent lower with significant falls for wheat, potatoes, fresh vegetables and milk.

9 The output value of cereals rose by £169 million (8.4 per cent). Despite the fall in price, the value of wheat increased by £264 million (22 per cent) as production returned to more normal levels following the impact of the wet weather on the 2001 harvest.

10 The value of livestock production increased by £434 million (8.3 per cent) as it recovered from the Foot and Mouth Disease outbreak. Sheep showed a marked improvement with prices up by 21 per cent, value by £215 million (34 per cent) and volume by 11 per cent.

11 Total subsidies less taxes on product in 2002 amounted to £2.1 billion, 7.7 per cent more than in 2001. Full details can be found in Chapter 8.

12 Intermediate consumption fell by £99 million or 1.2 per cent, due primarily to a fall of £148 million for animal feed. Consumption of energy changed very little but prices fell, resulting in reduced expenditure. Expenditure on other items was similar to 2001.

13 Gross Value Added for the industry, which represents its contribution to national GDP, increased in volume by 12 per cent and value by 3.9 per cent, driven by an increase in output and a decrease in intermediate consumption.

14 Net Value Added at factor cost is the best measure of value added by the industry because it includes all subsidies (some are not included in output e.g. set-aside and agri-environment). It makes no allowance for interest, rent or labour costs. It increased by 5.0 per cent.

15 TIFF is derived by deducting interest, rent and paid labour costs from Net Value Added at factor cost. Interest payments were 13 per cent lower with rent and labour costs virtually unchanged; as a consequence TIFF showed a rise.

Balance sheets   16 The aggregate balance sheets for UK agriculture, Table 6.3, show the net worth of
(Table 6.3)   the industry in terms of assets and liabilities at the end of each calendar year.

17 Revised figures confirm that assets, liabilities and net worth all increased in 2000. The increase in net worth forecast for 2001 is borne out by the latest figures. Foot and Mouth Disease compensation payments have both increased assets and reduced liabilities.

18 The value of land and buildings, which forms the major proportion of the value of

assets, increased by 4.1 per cent. The price of land increased in 2001 although the number of sales fell. The value of breeding livestock rose (up 9.2 per cent) while trading livestock values fell (down 9.6 per cent). The numbers of all types of breeding livestock fell, but prices, and consequently values, of cattle and sheep increased. Only the price and value of pigs declined. The values of store pigs and sheep (trading livestock) each fell by around 30 per cent, while the value of store cattle fell by around seven per cent. The value of poultry, which is included in trading livestock, rose by five per cent. The value of other assets hardly changed.

Percentage change	Current prices		Real terms	
	1999/2000	2000/2001	1999/2000	2000/2001
Total assets	2.4	3.4	-0.5	2.7
Total liabilities	1.3	-3.4	-1.6	-4.1
Net worth	2.6	4.1	-0.4	3.4

Current prices are net of depreciation but exclude the value of quotas.

Real terms at 1995 prices.

19 Total liabilities fell by 3.4 per cent, with long and medium-term liabilities falling more than short-term ones (down 3.9 per cent and 3.0 per cent respectively). Bank loans are the largest item within long and medium-term liabilities; they decreased by 6.6 per cent. Bank overdrafts (short-term loans) also fell significantly, by 5.2 per cent.

20 Surveys carried out in 2001 indicate that restocking of farms was not complete by the end of the year. Some effects of the disease outbreak in 2001 may still be apparent in the balance sheets for 2002 which will be published in the following year.

21 Net worth has now reached its highest value in real terms since 1980, as have total assets. Liabilities are at their lowest value since the same year.

Net worth (real terms 1995 prices)
£ billion

22 Values of land and buildings are not directly comparable with data prior to 1993. From 1993, for England and Wales, some transactions influenced by non-market considerations have been excluded. The new price series may not necessarily represent purely competitive conditions. However, in general it tends to be higher than the old series. In addition, land and buildings are now valued using the average price of land sold. As a result of both these changes, land and buildings (and consequently total assets) tend to have a higher valuation than previously. Due to the provisional nature of the published land price series, a weighted average of the land price in quarter 3 and quarter 4 of the balance sheet year is used to value land and buildings.

Accumulation accounts

23 Tables 6.4 and 6.5 form part of the accumulation accounts for the agriculture industry. The accumulation accounts include the capital account, the other changes in the volume of assets account, the revaluation account and the financial account. Table 6.4 contains elements of the capital account and the other changes in the volume of assets account. Table 6.5 shows elements of the revaluation account and

changes in net worth due to changes in prices. The net worth shown in the balance sheets incorporates changes due to all of the accumulation accounts.

Capital account
(Table 6.4)

24 The capital account, table 6.4, shows estimates of changes in the assets held by the UK agricultural sector.

25 The revised estimate of total Gross Fixed Capital Formation in non-livestock assets for 2001 is £1.4 billion, or an increase of 18 per cent. The provisional estimate of total Gross Fixed Capital Formation in buildings, works, plant, machinery and vehicles in 2002 is £1.6 billion. This is an increase of 12 per cent over 2001. The increase is thought to be mainly due to Foot and Mouth Disease payments being spent both on livestock and non-livestock investment. However, Gross Fixed Capital Formation is still about 20 per cent lower than in the 1990s. Consumption of fixed non-livestock assets decreased slightly between 2001 and 2002.

26 Capital formation and capital consumption in livestock measure the output value due to the production of breeding animals and the depreciation of breeding animals (mainly dairy cows, beef cows, ewes, sows and egg-laying poultry). In 2001 production of breeding cattle, sheep and pigs increased due to restocking after Foot and Mouth Disease. In 2002 the value of capital formation in livestock increased by £126 million mainly due to increases in prices for breeding animals. In contrast, consumption of fixed capital in livestock (approximated by assuming that all depreciation takes place at the time animals leave the breeding herds) increased by only £62 million. Net capital formation in livestock is estimated to be postive in 2002 for the first time since 1998.

27 Changes in inventories contribute to income. Stocks of crops were higher than in 2001 because of the recovery in production of cereals and other crops. Stocks of work-in-progress animals were lower. In 2001, animals destroyed due to Foot and Mouth Disease measures have not been removed from the inventories but have been shown as exceptional losses. In 2002 some animals originally intended for slaughter were retained for breeding; thus cattle and breeding sheep increased at the expense of animals for slaughter.

28 Table 6.4 also brings together information on the balance sheet value of Foot and Mouth Disease losses and the value of compensation and welfare disposal payments (see paragraph 4 in this chapter). Capital transfers to the UK agriculture industry amounted to £1.4 billion in 2001, of which Foot and Mouth Disease payments accounted for £1.3 billion. Livestock destroyed due to Foot and Mouth Disease measures are treated as exceptional losses and should be deducted from within the capital account. These balance sheet losses have been valued at £0.5 billion but the figure is not comparable to that for payments. The balance sheet valuation is based on a macro approach using the number of animals destroyed and estimated average market prices.

29 It is not yet possible to show the impact of Foot and Mouth Disease on the net worth of the industry. The EU auditors and NAO studies of Foot and Mouth Disease payments, together with our own study, will provide information on the compensation process. The NAO study was published on 21 June 2002 (www.nao.gov.uk). The report concluded:

- "Problems with the slaughter compensation scheme increased the Department's costs."
- "The attempt to set standard rates for compensation contributed to a rise in prices. Standard rates for slaughtered animals were introduced on 22 March 2001 because the valuation process was thought to be delaying the slaughter of animals on infected premises."
- "The Livestock Welfare Disposal Scheme helped many farmers but the generous rates created demand that exceeded initial capacity."

30 The EU auditor's report and the Defra study had not been published when this publication went to print. It is hoped that an updated estimate of the valuation will be published in "Agriculture in the United Kingdom 2003".

31 For details of the valuation in the balance sheets and details on the Foot and Mouth Disease compensation and welfare disposal payments, see "Agriculture in the United Kingdom 2001".

Accumulation accounts: Stock appreciation
(Table 6.5)

32 Table 6.5 shows estimates of stock appreciation in the industry. Stock appreciation (holding gains) measures the change in value between the time of production and the end of the accounting period due to changes in price. It is not included in the production and income account of the Aggregate Agricultural Account and thus does not contribute to income.

33 Total stock appreciation in 2002 increased to £431 million. The value of livestock increased by £584 million due to increases in prices of animals after production had taken place. The increases in price are mainly due to a reduction in supply. The value of crops held in stock fell by £152 million.

Interest
(Table 6.6)

34 Table 6.6 shows details of interest charges payable on farmers' borrowings for agricultural purposes (including land purchases). These payments, net of interest on short-term deposits, are estimated to have decreased between 2001 and 2002 by 13 per cent to £479 million. The average interest rate in 2002 was lower than in the previous year which more than offset the effects of an increase in farmers' borrowings.

Volume of capital assets
(Table 6.7)

35 Table 6.7 shows volume indices for the formation and consumption of fixed capital assets (see also table 6.4). The total volume of Gross Fixed Capital Formation rose by 6.7 per cent in 2002 compared with 2001, whilst its value rose by 15 per cent. The total volume of consumption of fixed capital fell by 4.9 per cent but its value increased by 1.9 per cent due to increases in prices.

36 Within capital formation, plant and machinery are estimated to have experienced the largest increase in volume (up 12 per cent) but the volume of buildings and works and vehicles is also estimated to have increased, by more than 5 per cent. The increases in value are slightly higher than the increases in volume reflecting small increases in price.

37 The rise in the value of capital formation in livestock (up 21 per cent) is due to an increase in the price of breeding and dairy cattle and breeding sheep. The volume of

capital formation in livestock decreased slightly in 2002.

38 Between 1994 and 2000, the volume of capital formation in all non-livestock assets decreased every year. In the last two years however, the volume of capital formation in all non-livestock assets has increased but it remains below the levels of the 1990s.

39 Consumption of Fixed Capital (CFC) continued its downward trend. CFC in non-livestock assets has been declining since 1997. CFC in livestock is inherently more volatile. A sharp fall from 1996 to 1997 due to BSE (coinciding with an increase in capital formation in the same years) was followed by stagnation, then a large rise in 2000 followed by decreases in 2001 and 2002. The large fall in 2002 indicates that fewer capital animals were culled as the industry was still recovering from the Foot and Mouth Disease losses.

Table 6.1 Production and income account at current prices

Inquiries: Christine Jeannette on 01904 455080 email: christine.jeannette@defra.gsi.gov.uk

£ million   Calendar years

	Average of 1991-1993	1998	1999	2000	2001	2002 (provisional)
Output (a)						
1 Total cereals	2 587	2 502	2 326	2 337	2 023	2 192
wheat	1 718	1 652	1 525	1 578	1 226	1 490
rye	3	5	4	3	3	3
barley	805	781	735	686	725	623
oats and summer cereal mixtures	61	61	58	65	65	71
other cereals	2	3	4	5	4	5
2 Total industrial crops	1 012	1 012	1 012	791	817	884
oilseeds	460	485	503	283	291	299
oilseed rape	358	417	371	249	275	294
other oilseeds	102	68	132	34	16	6
sugar beet	350	298	280	252	256	272
other industrial crops	203	228	230	256	269	313
fibre plants	1	13	11	8	4	2
hops	20	14	13	11	10	11
others (b)	182	201	205	236	256	300
3 Total forage plants	167	141	144	138	170	164
4 Total vegetables and horticultural products	1 483	1 636	1 677	1 559	1 712	1 674
fresh vegetables	944	987	962	885	1 031	948
plants and flowers	539	650	714	674	681	726
5 Total potatoes (including seeds)	484	630	750	454	637	463
6 Total fruit	279	259	257	229	235	257
7 Other crop products including seeds	44	43	45	40	37	26
8 Total crop output (sum 1 - 7)	6 057	6 223	6 210	5 547	5 630	5 661
9 Total livestock production	6 358	6 087	5 631	5 583	5 232	5 666
primarily for meat	5 662	5 496	5 237	5 196	4 633	4 940
cattle	2 141	1 982	2 047	1 994	1 772	2 024
pigs	1 072	887	785	794	749	687
sheep	1 166	1 112	984	953	625	840
poultry	1 160	1 367	1 272	1 303	1 332	1 226
other animals	124	149	149	153	155	163
Gross Fixed Capital Formation	696	591	394	386	600	726
cattle	433	297	207	188	346	423
pigs	16	6	7	6	5	8
sheep	133	154	56	62	122	168
poultry	113	134	124	130	126	127
10 Total livestock products	3 431	3 135	3 045	2 809	3 267	3 007
milk	2 967	2 709	2 653	2 393	2 822	2 489
eggs	403	381	344	371	406	476
raw wool	38	24	21	23	17	19
other animal products	23	21	26	23	21	23
11 Total livestock output (9 + 10)	9 789	9 222	8 675	8 392	8 499	8 672

continued

Table 6.1 continued

£ million   Calendar Years

	Average of 1991-1993	1998	1999	2000	2001	2002 (provisional)
12 Total other agricultural activities	501	679	716	634	628	657
agricultural services	440	570	610	583	604	626
leasing-out quota	61	109	106	51	24	31
13 Total inseparable non-agricultural activities	270	421	430	436	583	518
14 Gross output at basic prices (8 + 11 + 12 + 13)	16 617	16 545	16 032	15 009	15 340	15 508
15 Total subsidies (less taxes) on product	1 076	2 436	2 373	2 187	1 912	2 060
16 Output at market prices (14 - 15)	15 541	14 109	13 659	12 822	13 428	13 448
of which						
transactions within the agricultural industry						
feed wheat	97	79	64	40	38	39
feed barley	251	164	148	137	151	137
feed oats	21	12	14	13	12	11
seed potatoes	17	12	30	9	13	13
straw	157	173	176	205	222	265
contract work	440	570	610	583	604	626
leasing of quota	61	109	106	51	24	31
total capital formation in livestock	696	591	394	386	600	726
Intermediate consumption						
17 Seeds	308	331	331	273	292	295
cereals	117	84	94	81	91	85
other	191	247	237	192	202	209
18 Energy	584	597	621	683	685	651
electricity	247	231	222	229	242	226
fuels	337	366	399	454	443	425
19 Fertilisers	823	832	756	738	761	754
20 Pesticides	541	655	622	581	534	527
21 Veterinary expenses	235	288	270	256	245	241
22 Animal feed	2 889	2 444	2 261	2 117	2 323	2 175
compounds (d)	1 723	1 524	1 402	1 285	1 401	1 365
straights (d)	798	667	632	642	719	623
feed purchased from other farms	368	254	227	189	202	187
23 Total maintenance (c)	907	1 025	1 017	943	988	1 022
materials	617	700	699	651	663	689
buildings	290	325	318	292	325	332
24 Agricultural services	440	570	610	583	604	626
25 Other goods and services (c) (e)	1 778	2 241	2 257	2 087	2 058	2 100
26 Total intermediate consumption (sum 17 - 25)	8 505	8 983	8 744	8 260	8 490	8 391

continued

Table 6.1 continued

£ million   Calendar Years

	Average of 1991-1993	1998	1999	2000	2001	2002 (provisional)
27 Gross value added at basic prices(14 - 26)	8 112	7 562	7 288	6 749	6 850	7 117
28 Total consumption of Fixed Capital	2 374	2 587	2 424	2 491	2 588	2 638
equipment	1 116	1 325	1 311	1 276	1 280	1 271
buildings (c) (f)	591	683	700	690	689	687
livestock	667	580	413	526	619	680
cattle	408	314	207	278	324	406
pigs	16	8	8	8	6	8
sheep	135	118	69	118	169	143
poultry	108	140	129	121	120	124
29 Net value added at basic prices (27 - 28)	5 738	4 974	4 864	4 258	4 263	4 479
30 Compensation of employees (g)	1 783	1 977	2 030	1 903	1 909	1 907
31 Other taxes on production	- 56	- 89	- 90	- 91	- 84	- 76
32 Other subsidies on production	87	231	329	326	574	587
animal disease compensation	8	24	28	41	28	37
set-aside	47	88	170	127	180	152
agri-environment schemes (h)	32	120	131	158	198	241
other including Less Favoured Areas schemes (i)	-	-	-	-	168	157
33 Net value added at factor cost (29 + 31 + 32)	5 768	5 117	5 103	4 492	4 752	4 990
34 Rent	171	250	238	222	250	248
rent paid (j)	171	331	321	301	329	347
rent received (k)	. ..	- 81	- 82	- 79	- 78	- 99
35 Interest (l)	692	681	595	624	551	479
36 Total income from farming (33 - 30 - 34 - 35)	3 122	2 210	2 240	1 742	2 041	2 356

source: Defra website, www.defra.gov.uk/esg

(a) Output is net of VAT collected on the sale of non-edible products. Figures for total output include subsidies on products, but not other subsidies.

(b) Includes straw and minor crops.

(c) Landlords' expenses are included within total maintenance, other goods and services and Consumption of Fixed Capital of buildings.

(d) For years prior to 1992 the split between compounds and straights has been estimated based on the split present in later years.

(e) Includes livestock and crop costs, water costs, insurance premiums, bank charges, professional fees, rates and other farming costs.

(f) A more empirically based methodology for calculating landlords' consumption of fixed capital was introduced in 2000. The new series has been linked with the old one using a smoothing procedure for the transition year of 1996.

(g) Excludes the value of work done by farm labour on own account capital formation in buildings and works.

(h) Includes Environmentally and Nitrate Sensitive Areas, Countryside Stewardship and other management schemes, and Moorland, Habitat, Farm Woodland and Organic Farming Schemes.

(i) Land area based schemes which replaced the Hill Livestock Compensatory Allowance Scheme in 2001. These are Tir Mynydd in Wales, Less Favoured Area Compensatory Scheme in Northern Ireland, Less Favoured Areas Support Scheme in Scotland and Hill Farm Allowance in England.

(j) Rent paid on all tenanted land (including 'conacre' land in Northern Ireland) less landlords' expenses, landlords' consumption of fixed capital and the benefit value of dwellings on that land.

(k) Rent received by farming landowners from renting of land to other farmers less landlords' expenses. This series starts in 1996 following a revision to the methodology of calculating net rent.

(l) Interest charges on loans for current farming purposes and buildings and works less interest on money held on short term deposit.

Chart 6.2 Changes in outputs and inputs

Changes in value of outputs and inputs between 2001 and 2002 (provisional)

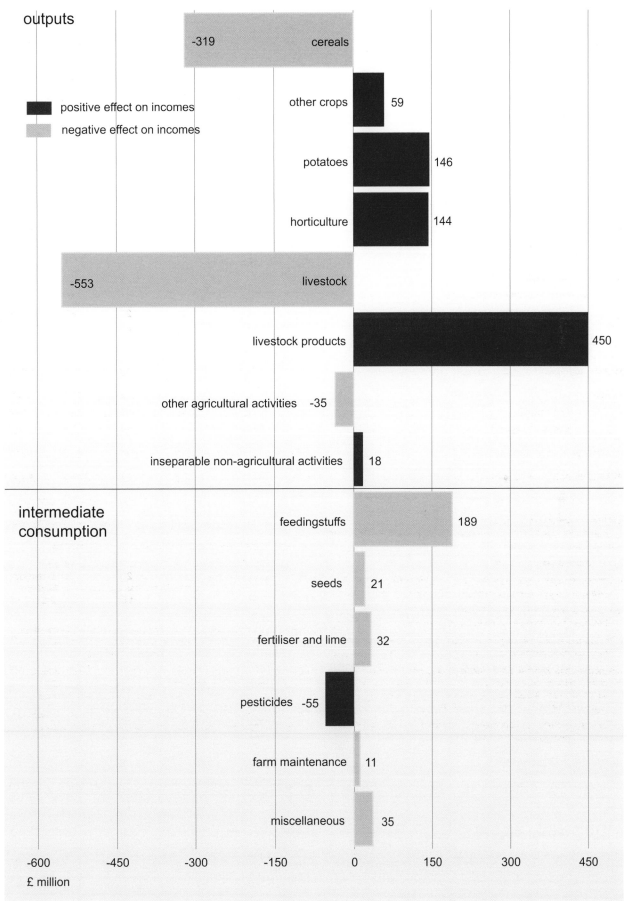

outputs

cereals -319

other crops 59

potatoes 146

horticulture 144

livestock -553

livestock products 450

other agricultural activities -35

inseparable non-agricultural activities 18

■ positive effect on incomes
▨ negative effect on incomes

intermediate consumption

feedingstuffs 189

seeds 21

fertiliser and lime 32

pesticides -55

farm maintenance 11

miscellaneous 35

-600   -450   -300   -150   0   150   300   450

£ million

Table 6.2 Changes in outputs and inputs

Inquiries: Christine Jeannette on 01904 455080 email: christine.jeannette@defra.gsi.gov.uk

£ million   Calendar years

	Current price value		Changes %		
	2001	2002	value	volume	price
Output (a)					
1 Total cereals	2023	2192	8	21	-11
wheat	1226	1490	22	38	-12
rye	3	3	11	-	11
barley	725	623	-14	-7	-8
oats and summer cereal mixtures	65	71	10	19	-8
other cereals	4	5	17	15	2
2 Total industrial crops	817	884	8	10	-2
oilseeds	291	299	3	19	-13
oilseed rape	275	294	7	23	-13
other oilseeds	16	6	-64	-53	-24
sugar beet	256	272	6	13	-6
other industrial crops	269	313	16	-1	17
fibre plants	4	2	-50	-49	-3
hops	10	11	8	5	3
others (b)	256	300	17	-	18
3 Total forage plants	170	164	-3	1	-4
4 Total vegetables and horticultural products	1712	1674	-2	4	-6
fresh vegetables	1031	948	-8	5	-12
plants and flowers	681	726	7	2	4
5 Total potatoes (including seeds)	637	463	-27	-3	-25
6 Total fruit	235	257	9	-3	12
7 Other crop products including seeds	37	26	-30	-30	-
8 Total crop output (sum 1 - 7)	5630	5661	1	10	-8
9 Total livestock production	5232	5666	8	4	4
primarily for meat	4633	4940	7	5	2
cattle	1772	2024	14	12	2
pigs	749	687	-8	-4	-5
sheep	625	840	34	11	21
poultry	1332	1226	-8	-4	-4
other animals	155	163	5	-	5
Gross Fixed Capital Formation	600	726	21	-	22
cattle	346	423	22	-2	25
pigs	5	8	50	62	-7
sheep	122	168	37	7	28
poultry	126	127	1	-5	6
10 Total livestock products	3267	3007	-8	2	-10
milk	2822	2489	-12	1	-13
eggs	406	476	17	7	9
raw wool	17	19	8	4	3
other animal products	21	23	8	6	2
11 Total livestock output (9 + 10)	8499	8672	2	3	-1

continued

Table 6.2 continued

£ million

	Current price value		Changes %		
	2001	2002	value	volume	price
12 Total other agricultural activities	628	657	5	2	3
agricultural services	604	626	4	4	-
leasing out quota	24	31	29	-33	93
13 Total inseparable non-agricultural activities	583	518	-11	-14	3
14 Gross output at basic prices (8 + 11 + 12 + 13)	15340	15508	1	5	-4
15 Total subsidies (less taxes) on product	1912	2060	8	14	-5
16 Output at market prices (14 - 15)	13428	13448	-	4	-3
of which					
transactions within the agricultural industry					
feed wheat	38	39	-	21	-17
feed barley	151	137	-10	2	-11
feed oats	12	11	-8	3	-11
seed potatoes	13	13	-1	12	-12
straw	222	265	19	-	20
contract work	604	626	4	4	-
leasing of quota	24	31	29	-33	93
total capital formation in livestock	600	726	21	-	22
Intermediate consumption					
17 Seeds	292	295	1	-3	4
cereals	91	85	-6	-2	-4
other	202	209	4	-3	7
18 Energy	685	651	-5	-	-5
electricity	242	226	-7	-2	-5
fuels	443	425	-4	2	-5
19 Fertilisers	761	754	-1	7	-7
20 Pesticides	534	527	-1	4	-5
21 Veterinary expenses	245	241	-2	-	-1
22 Animal feed	2323	2175	-6	-4	-3
compounds (d)	1401	1365	-3	-2	-1
straights (d)	719	623	-13	-10	-4
feed purchased from other farms	202	187	-8	5	-12
23 Total maintenance (c)	988	1022	3	-	3
materials	663	689	4	-1	5
buildings	325	332	2	1	1
24 Agricultural services	604	626	4	4	-
25 Other goods and services (c) (e)	2058	2100	2	-2	4
26 Total intermediate consumption (sum 17 - 25)	8490	8391	-1	-	-1
27 Gross value added at basic prices(14 - 26)	6850	7117	4	12	-7

continued

Table 6.2 continued

£ million   Calendar Years

	Current price value		Changes %		
	2001	2002	value	volume	price
28 Total consumption of fixed capital	2588	2638	2	-5	7
equipment	1280	1271	-1	-2	2
buildings (c) (f)	689	687	-	-2	2
livestock	619	680	10	-12	25
cattle	324	406	25	-4	31
pigs	6	8	27	46	-13
sheep	169	143	-16	-34	29
poultry	120	124	3	-6	9
29 Net value added at basic prices (27 - 28)	4263	4479	5	..	..
30 Compensation of employees (g)	1909	1907	-	-5	5
31 Other taxes on production	-84	-76	-10	..	..
32 Other subsidies on production	574	587	2	..	..
animal disease compensation	28	37	35	..	..
set-aside	180	152	-15	..	..
agri-environment schemes (h)	198	241	21	..	..
other including Less Favoured Areas schemes (i)	168	157	-6	..	..
33 Net value added at factor cost (29 + 31 + 32)	4752	4990	5	..	..
34 Rent	250	248	-1	..	..
rent paid (j)	329	347	5	..	..
rent received (k)	-78	-99	26	..	..
35 Interest (l)	551	479	-13	..	..
36 Total income from farming (33 - 30 - 34 - 35)	2041	2356	15	..	..

source: Defra website, www.defra.gov.uk/esg

(a) Output is net of VAT collected on the sale of non-edible products. Figures for total output include subsidies on products, but not other subsidies.

(b) Includes straw and minor crops.

(c) Landlords' expenses are included within total maintenance, other goods and services and Consumption of Fixed Capital of buildings.

(d) For years prior to 1992 the split between compounds and straights has been estimated based on the split present in later years.

(e) Includes livestock and crop costs, water costs, insurance premiums, bank charges, professional fees, rates and other farming costs.

(f) A more empirically based methodology for calculating landlords' consumption of fixed capital was introduced in 2000. The new series has been linked with the old one using a smoothing procedure for the transition year of 1996.

(g) Excludes the value of work done by farm labour on own account capital formation in buildings and works.

(h) Includes Environmentally and Nitrate Sensitive Areas, Countryside Stewardship and other management schemes, and Moorland, Habitat, Farm Woodland and Organic Farming Schemes.

(i) Land area based schemes which replaced the Hill Livestock Compensatory Allowance Scheme in 2001. These are Tir Mynydd in Wales, Less Favoured Area Compensatory Scheme in Northern Ireland, Less Favoured Areas Support Scheme in Scotland and Hill Farm Allowance in England.

(j) Rent paid on all tenanted land (including 'conacre' land in Northern Ireland) less landlords' expenses, landlords' consumption of fixed capital and the benefit value of dwellings on that land.

(k) Rent received by farming landowners from renting of land to other farmers less landlords' expenses. This series starts in 1996 following a revision to the methodology of calculating net rent.

(l) Interest charges on loans for current farming purposes and buildings and works less interest on money held on short term deposit.

Table 6.3 Aggregate balance sheets for United Kingdom agriculture

Inquiries: Barbara Boize on 01904 455081 email: barbara.boize@defra.gsi.gov.uk

£ million   Calendar years

	Average of 1991-1993	1998	1999	2000	2001 (provisional)
At current prices					
Assets					
Fixed (a):					
Land and buildings (b)	41 410	85 076	90 784	92 767	96 539
Plant, machinery and vehicles	6 698	8 247	7 892	7 628	7 578
Breeding livestock	5 595	3 799	2 824	3 668	4 004
Total fixed	53 702	97 121	101 499	104 062	108 121
Current:					
Trading livestock	3 198	2 155	2 231	2 094	1 892
Crops and stores	2 436	2 593	2 139	2 241	2 229
Debtors, cash deposits	2 789	3 817	4 063	4 223	4 240
Total current	8 423	8 565	8 433	8 557	8 361
Total Assets	62 125	105 686	109 932	112 619	116 482
Liabilities (c) (d)					
Long and medium term:					
AMC, SASC, and LIC (e)	843	1 321	1 381	1 405	1 380
Building societies and institutions	154	299	336	401	410
Bank loans	1 305	2 234	2 350	2 372	2 216
Family loans	300	385	421	429	429
Other	165	185	189	218	202
Total long and medium term	2 767	4 424	4 676	4 825	4 638
Short term:					
Leasing	520	186	136	95	94
Hire purchase	247	489	461	478	466
Trade credit	1 137	1 208	1 289	1 297	1 317
Bank overdrafts	3 267	2 812	3 048	3 038	2 881
Other	91	126	115	119	118
Total short-term	5 262	4 821	5 050	5 027	4 876
Total liabilities	8 028	9 245	9 726	9 852	9 514
Net worth	54 097	96 441	100 206	102 767	106 968
In real terms (as deflated by the RPI):					
Indices, 1995 = 100					
Total assets	73	105	108	107	110
Total liabilities	103	100	104	102	98
Net worth	70	106	108	108	111

source: Defra website, www.defra.gov.uk/esg

(a) The valuations of land, buildings and breeding livestock are at average market prices; those of plant, machinery and vehicles are replacement cost, net of depreciation.

(b) Includes the value of owner-occupied and tenanted land and excludes dwelling houses apart from a proportion attributed to business use. Values of land and buildings are not directly comparable with data prior to 1993. From 1993, for England and Wales, some transactions influenced by non-market considerations have been excluded.

(c) Financial estimates are derived in part from a year-end analysis of farms in the Farm Business Survey. In practice, year-ends vary from December through to April, with concentrations of year-ends at end-December and end-March.

(d) Values for some liabilities are not strictly comparable with corresponding data prior to 1991. The revisions have resulted in an estimated increase of 8-9 per cent in net worth in 1991 and 1992.

(e) Agricultural Mortgage Company (AMC), Scottish Agricultural Securities Corporation (SASC) and Land Improvement Company (LIC).

Table 6.4 Capital account

Inquiries: Christine Jeannette on 01904 455080 email: christine.jeannette@defra.gsi.gov.uk

£ million					Calendar years	
	Average of 1991-1993	1998	1999	2000	2001	2002 (provisional)
Gross fixed capital formation	2 135	2 007	1 644	1 591	2 024	2 318
Acquisitions less disposals of non-livestock assets:	1 439	1 416	1 250	1 204	1 424	1 592
buildings and works	455	505	371	344	426	458
plant and machinery	806	728	712	686	808	927
vehicles	178	183	167	174	190	207
Capital formation in livestock (a):	696	591	394	386	600	726
cattle	433	297	207	188	346	423
sheep	133	154	56	62	122	168
pigs	16	6	7	6	5	8
poultry	113	134	124	130	126	127
Consumption of fixed capital	2 374	2 587	2 424	2 491	2 588	2 638
Non-livestock assets:	1 707	2 008	2 011	1 966	1 969	1 958
buildings and works	591	683	700	690	689	687
plant and machinery	941	1 104	1 091	1 065	1 078	1 068
vehicles	175	221	220	211	203	203
Livestock (b):	667	580	413	526	619	680
cattle	408	314	207	278	324	406
sheep	135	118	69	118	169	143
pigs	16	8	8	8	6	8
poultry	108	140	129	121	120	124
Changes in inventories	- 22	- 97	25	- 77	- 34	59
stocks of crops	- 8	- 87	29	7	- 67	103
work-in-progress livestock	- 13	- 10	- 4	- 84	33	- 44
Total Income from Farming	3 122	2 210	2 240	1 742	2 041	2 356
Capital transfers	138	83	25	19	1 396	32
Foot and Mouth Disease payments:	..	..	..	..	1 313	-
culled cattle	..	..	..	..	675	..
culled sheep	..	..	..	..	414	..
culled pigs	..	..	..	..	15	..
welfare disposals of cattle	..	..	..	..	125	-
welfare disposals of sheep	..	..	..	..	64	..
welfare disposals of pigs	..	..	..	..	15	..
other livestock (culled and welfare)	..	..	..	..	5	..
Other capital transfers	91	74	18	12	75	24
Capital grants	47	9	7	7	8	8
Exceptional disposals (due to Foot and Mouth Disease) (c):	..	..	..	..	465	..
breeding cattle	..	..	..	..	177	..
slaughter cattle	..	..	..	..	121	..
breeding sheep	..	..	..	..	91	..
slaughter sheep	..	..	..	..	53	..
breeding pigs	..	..	..	..	4	..
slaughter pigs	..	..	..	..	14	..
other livestock	..	..	..	..	5	..

source: Defra website, www.defra.gov.uk/esg

Table 6.4 continued

(a) Capital formation in livestock is estimated by valuing the number of entries to the breeding herds at the entry price less the disposal price.

(b) Consumption of fixed capital in livestock is estimated by valuing the disposals from the breeding herds at the entry price less the disposal price.

(c) Livestock culled due to Foot and Mouth Disease measures are treated as exceptional losses as defined in the European System of Accounts 1995.

Table 6.5 Stock appreciation

Inquiries: Christine Jeannette on 01904 455080 email: christine.jeannette@defra.gsi.gov.uk

£ million — Calendar years

	1998	1999	2000	2001	2002 (provisional)
Livestock production work-in-progress (non-breeders)					
cattle	- 158	89	- 78	- 56	295
sheep	- 84	35	12	- 47	75
pigs	- 58	40	99	- 69	41
poultry (a)	- 5	- 8	6	- 4	1
total	- 305	156	38	- 176	412
Replacement animals for breeding herds					
cattle	- 120	- 23	23	131	140
sheep	- 35	15	5	- 27	32
pigs	- 1	1	1	- 1	1
total	- 156	- 8	30	103	172
Crop production work-in-progress					
wheat	- 36	- 63	- 40	99	- 138
barley	4	- 21	- 5	- 1	- 16
potatoes	-	-	- 1	-	- 1
other crops (b)	- 14	- 37	13	10	3
total	- 46	- 122	- 32	108	- 152
Total stock appreciation	- 507	26	36	35	431

source: Defra website, www.defra.gov.uk/esg

(a) Broilers, ducks, geese and turkeys.

(b) Oats, oilseeds, apples and pears.

Table 6.6 Interest

Inquiries: Christine Jeannette on 01904 455080 email: christine.jeannette@defra.gsi.gov.uk

£ million (unless otherwise specified)   Calendar years

	Average of 1991-1993	1998	1999	2000	2001	2002 (provisional)
Interest rates						
average bank base lending rate in the UK	9.1%	7.2%	5.3%	6.0%	5.1%	4.0%
average rate of interest on bank advances to agriculture	11.7%	9.7%	7.7%	8.2%	7.3%	6.2%
Interest charges (all lending to the farm business) on:						
bank advances	523	483	409	441	377	..
Agricultural Mortgage Company loans	108	113	109	119	110	..
instalment credit	26	69	53	48	44	..
leased assets	32	15	10	7	6	..
other credit (a)	42	48	50	48	51	..
less interest on deposits (b)	39	48	37	39	36	..
Total	692	681	595	624	551	479

source: Defra website, www.defra.gov.uk/esg

(a) Interest paid on other institutional credit and that from private sources.

(b) Interest earned on money held on short-term deposit.

Table 6.7 Changes in volume of capital assets

Inquiries: Christine Jeannette on 01904 455080 email: christine.jeannette@defra.gsi.gov.uk

Calendar years

	Average of 1991-1993	1998	1999	2000	2001	2002 (provisional)
Total volume of Gross Fixed Capital Formation						
Indices 1995=100						
Gross fixed capital formation:	84.5	75.2	66.9	61.6	71.2	75.9
non livestock:	79.1	65.8	56.9	53.8	62.0	68.2
buildings and works	95.2	89.6	63.1	54.7	66.6	70.7
plant and machinery	74.4	55.9	54.1	51.8	58.1	65.3
vehicles	70.1	63.4	57.8	62.6	71.1	77.7
livestock	96.9	107.9	103.9	88.0	102.4	101.9
Total volume of capital consumption						
Indices 1995=100						
Consumption of fixed capital	96.5	99.7	98.0	96.9	95.1	90.5
non livestock:	100.0	99.8	97.9	95.0	93.8	91.7
buildings and works	99.7	100.3	98.7	94.9	96.9	95.2
plant and machinery	100.9	98.2	96.0	93.1	89.8	87.1
vehicles	95.9	106.2	105.7	105.2	105.1	105.6
livestock	89.3	99.6	98.2	105.8	101.4	88.9

source: Defra website, www.defra.gov.uk/esg

Chapter 7 Productivity

Introduction **1** A key measure of agriculture's economic performance is its productivity; that is, how well the agricultural industry uses the resources that are available to turn inputs into outputs. Productivity measures are based on the ratio of the volume of outputs and the volume of inputs. Productivity is a key measure of the economic sustainability of UK farming and food. It is an important driver of farm incomes and it is an essential foundation for the environmental and social contributions which farming and food make. However, measuring productivity is not straightforward and comparisons need to be interpreted carefully both because of practical problems in obtaining robust data and also because productivity performance, particularly in agriculture, is often shaped by exogenous factors - to do with climate, topography and location for example - which are not easily susceptible to change.

Volume Indices **2** The volume indices in table 7.1 have been revised back to 1973. The revisions are
(Table 7.1) due to a switch from Laspeyres indices to Fischer indices following recommendations by the OECD and Eurostat.

3 The volume of production has been fairly stable since the mid-1980s following a period of output growth in the late seventies and early eighties. Within total output however, there were largely different trends. Production of wheat, oilseeds, sugar beet and poultry has increased since 1985. Production of barley, fruit, vegetables, cattle, pigs, sheep and milk has decreased over the same period.

4 The volume of output in 2002 was 4.8 per cent higher than in 2001, due mainly to increases in crop and livestock production of wheat and livestock. In 2002 production of cereals was 21 per cent higher than in 2001, but remained below the volume of production in 2000. This was mainly due to the recovery in wheat production, which increased by 38 per cent. The volume of production of barley fell by 6.8 per cent. The volume of production of industrial crops increased by 10 per cent in 2002.

5 Vegetable production increased by 5.1 per cent in 2002. Fruit production fell by 2.6 per cent, continuing the declining long-term trend. The volume of output of potatoes decreased by 3.0 per cent in 2002 compared to 2001.

6 Production of livestock (mainly for meat processing) increased by 4.6 per cent in 2002 but was 5.4 per cent below 2000 production. Production of cattle and sheep increased by more than 10 per cent as the industry recovered from the effects of the Foot and Mouth Disease outbreak in 2001. Since 1998 pig production has decreased by more than 30 per cent. In 2002 this trend continued with a 3.7 per cent fall. The volume of production of poultry fell back to just above its 2000 level. Cattle and calves which were disposed of in the Over Thirty Month Scheme and the

Calf Processing Aid Scheme (which ran from 22 April 1996 until 31 July 1999) have not been counted towards the volume of output. Foot and Mouth Disease losses were treated as exceptional. This means that the volume of part-produced animals - for slaughter or the breeding herd - that were culled, are included in output.

7 Milk production has been fairly steady since 1991 due to the quota system. Production of eggs has increased since 1999. It increased by a further 7 per cent in 2002.

8 The revised estimate for 2001 for total inseparable non-agricultural activities showed an increase of 28 per cent. This large rise, mainly due to cleaning and disinfecting of farms affected by Foot and Mouth Disease, was above the long-term trend. The provisional figure for 2002 dropped back by 15 per cent bringing it back to the long-term increasing trend.

9 Overall the volume of inputs increased steadily up to 1998. In the late 1990s, the volume of inputs fell significantly due to pressures to reduce costs. Since 2000 inputs have stayed at roughly the same level. Consumption of seeds declined by 2.7 per cent in 2002, falling back to more normal levels after exceptionally high consumption in 2001 that were due to a high level of re-sowing. There were increases in consumption of both pesticides and fertilisers, reflecting the recovery in crop production this year. Animal feed consumption fell by 3.7 per cent in line with falling livestock numbers.

10 As a result of the rise in outputs in 2002, and with little change in the volume of inputs, Gross Value Added increased by 12 per cent.

Productivity
(Table 7.2 and Chart 7.1)

11 Productivity shows how efficiently inputs are converted into outputs. Since 1973 the productivity of the agricultural industry in the UK has increased by 43 per cent - see Chart 7.1 and Table 7.2. The measure used - total factor productivity - shows the volume of output leaving the industry per unit of all inputs, including fixed

Chart 7.1 Total factor productivity (final output per unit of all inputs)

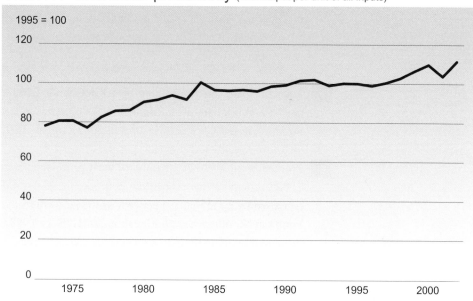

capital and paid labour; it encompasses all businesses engaged in farming activities, including specialist contractors. Increases in labour productivity have been the key factor driving this growth; since 1973 labour productivity has more than doubled. Labour productivity measures the volume of net value added per unit of all labour (paid and entrepreneurial).

Outputs
1995 = 100

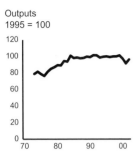

12 The increase in productivity in the 1970s and 1980s is explained by an increase in output without corresponding increases in inputs (including capital and labour). Throughout the 1990s, output remained static but inputs, especially labour, have decreased.

Inputs
1995 = 100

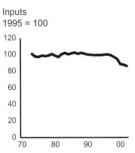

13 In 2002 output increased and inputs (including labour) declined slightly compared to the previous year. Thus, labour productivity increased by 28 per cent, whilst total factor productivity increased by 7.4 per cent. The reason for the large productivity gains compared to last year is that productivity was unusually low in 2001 when Foot and Mouth Disease and wet weather led to a large fall in productivity. In 2002, productivity measures have returned to their long-term trends.

Paid labour 14
(Table 7.3)

Table 7.3 shows the cost and volume of paid labour relating to agricultural work only, excluding time spent on the construction of farm buildings. The total cost of paid labour hardly changed in 2002, arising from a decrease in the volume of paid labour input of 4.6 per cent and an average salary increase of 4.7 per cent. The volume of total labour decreased by 3.8 per cent during 2002.

Paid labour volume
AWU

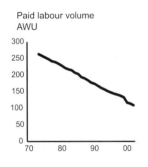

15 The most significant fall in inputs was in compensation of employees (or paid labour) which has reduced by 59 per cent since 1973, reflecting the outflow of labour from the industry.

16 Since the early 1980s there has been a shift in the composition of the labour force with an increase in part-time workers - rising from 25 per cent to about 50 per cent of the total by 2002.

Table 7.1 Output and input volume indices

Inquiries: Christine Jeannette on 01904 455080 email: christine.jeannette@defra.gsi.gov.uk

Indices 1995=100   Calendar years

	Average of 1991-1993	1998	1999	2000	2001	2002 (provisional)
Outputs (a)						
1 Total cereals	96.7	103.2	100.1	108.4	86.6	104.9
wheat	97.4	107.5	103.4	116.3	81.1	112.0
rye	78.6	82.1	82.1	78.6	82.1	82.1
barley	97.1	95.7	94.8	93.8	96.1	89.6
oats and summer cereal mixtures	79.4	95.0	87.0	103.4	99.2	118.3
other cereals	100.4	98.5	146.0	176.2	121.5	139.4
2 Total industrial crops	104.8	113.2	120.5	86.0	82.9	91.3
oilseeds	124.8	139.8	161.6	81.8	83.7	99.4
oilseed rape	108.9	134.9	134.7	93.0	96.2	118.0
other oilseeds	240.0	177.6	374.9	52.9	47.7	22.6
sugar beet	112.7	118.6	125.5	107.7	98.9	111.9
other industrial crops	73.3	74.3	66.6	67.9	64.3	63.9
fibre plants	4.6	109.0	106.8	69.5	48.0	24.5
hops	129.9	81.9	69.8	62.8	56.8	59.8
others (b)	73.1	72.6	65.0	68.1	65.1	64.9
3 Total forage plants	127.1	110.2	116.8	123.1	144.8	146.2
4 Total vegetables and horticultural products	106.8	97.2	99.2	97.0	91.5	95.1
fresh vegetables	110.6	98.4	99.3	92.8	86.7	91.2
plants and flowers	100.6	95.0	98.5	102.2	97.7	100.0
5 Total potatoes (including seeds)	107.7	90.4	107.2	94.6	96.3	93.5
6 Total fruit	126.2	89.4	92.8	84.3	88.2	85.9
7 Other crop products including seeds	112.7	91.5	101.4	98.5	96.6	67.3
8 Total crop output (sum 1 - 7)	103.2	101.8	104.5	100.1	90.4	99.0
9 Total livestock production	97.5	97.9	96.0	91.0	84.2	87.5
mainly for meat processing	97.6	97.0	95.3	91.2	82.4	86.2
cattle	99.2	83.6	84.6	82.1	72.9	81.7
pigs	101.5	112.2	102.4	86.3	79.2	76.3
sheep	104.3	99.7	98.8	94.6	67.6	74.9
poultry	86.7	108.6	106.0	106.4	110.9	106.8
other animals	99.1	102.3	101.7	101.7	101.4	101.8
Gross Fixed Capital Formation	96.9	107.9	103.9	88.0	102.4	101.9
cattle	95.4	96.0	96.6	84.4	97.8	95.5
pigs	115.9	87.1	97.4	66.5	54.9	88.8
sheep	96.9	122.7	92.4	60.9	97.2	104.1
poultry	95.8	123.7	130.2	119.6	114.8	108.8
10 Total livestock products	101.0	99.6	101.3	99.2	101.4	103.6
milk	100.5	99.0	101.4	98.6	99.9	101.2
eggs	104.0	105.5	101.8	105.5	116.6	124.8
raw wool	103.5	103.3	95.3	91.7	76.2	79.5
other animal products	108.4	80.7	95.7	80.4	71.3	75.8
11 Total livestock output (9 + 10)	98.7	98.5	97.9	93.8	89.9	92.9

continued

Table 7.1 continued
Indices 1995 = 100

	Average of 1991-1993	1998	1999	2000	2001	2002 (provisional)
12 Total other agricultural activities	89.0	116.2	123.9	116.8	122.4	124.3
agricultural services	93.9	115.2	123.2	115.5	119.7	124.0
leasing out quota	69.8	121.8	127.8	125.5	156.9	105.0
13 Total inseparable non-agricultural activities	91.4	118.1	118.9	116.2	150.7	130.2
14 Gross output at basic prices (8 + 11 + 12 + 13)	99.8	100.9	101.8	97.6	92.8	97.2
15 Total subsidies (less taxes) on product	106.9	105.6	106.7	98.8	84.7	96.2
16 Output at market prices (14 - 15)	99.2	100.1	101.0	97.3	94.0	97.4
of which						
transactions within the agricultural industry						
feed wheat	164.2	209.9	175.0	120.1	103.0	124.1
feed barley	117.5	123.5	113.6	112.2	121.1	123.2
feed oats	100.6	100.1	118.2	108.8	105.5	108.2
seed potatoes	119.1	79.3	84.4	76.2	60.0	67.5
straw	70.3	69.5	61.0	64.4	61.2	60.9
contract work	93.9	115.2	123.2	115.5	119.7	124.0
leasing of quota	69.8	121.8	127.8	125.5	156.9	105.0
total capital formation in livestock	96.8	108.2	104.2	88.3	102.7	102.2
Intermediate consumption						
17 Seeds	98.6	94.8	95.7	93.2	98.1	95.5
cereals	98.5	83.1	93.0	83.2	91.0	89.5
other	98.4	100.1	97.2	98.1	101.6	98.4
18 Energy	101.8	108.0	102.8	90.2	93.8	94.2
electricity	100.6	106.9	100.3	91.8	100.8	99.2
fuels	102.7	108.9	104.7	89.7	90.7	92.2
19 Fertilisers	103.2	107.9	101.0	88.4	82.4	88.2
20 Pesticides	96.5	111.3	108.6	106.9	101.6	105.7
21 Veterinary expenses	82.4	96.3	90.2	86.4	84.1	83.8
22 Animal feed	94.8	94.7	95.4	91.1	93.5	90.0
compounds (d)	96.4	94.9	97.5	89.8	92.6	90.7
straights (d)	82.8	83.6	84.0	88.2	89.8	81.2
feed purchased from other farms	125.5	139.8	126.5	113.8	116.5	122.6
23 Total maintenance (c)	93.2	88.8	87.1	79.1	80.9	81.0
materials	96.5	91.2	89.1	81.2	80.4	79.9
buildings	86.7	84.0	83.1	75.1	82.2	83.4
24 Agricultural services	93.9	115.2	123.2	115.5	119.7	124.0
25 Other goods and services (c) (e)	93.7	99.6	96.8	88.5	86.4	84.9
26 Total intermediate consumption (sum 17 - 25)	95.3	99.4	97.8	90.7	90.7	90.4
27 Gross value added at basic prices(14 - 26)	104.4	103.0	107.1	106.8	95.3	106.2

continued

Table 7.1 continued
Indices 1995 = 100

	Average of 1991-1993	1998	1999	2000	2001	2002 (provisional)
28 Total Consumption of Fixed Capital	96.5	99.7	98.0	96.9	95.1	90.5
equipment	100.1	99.5	97.5	95.0	92.2	89.9
buildings (c) (f)	99.7	100.3	98.7	94.9	96.9	95.2
livestock	89.3	99.6	98.2	105.8	101.4	88.9
cattle	87.7	92.3	94.0	106.7	91.9	88.1
pigs	103.6	108.2	97.5	82.6	56.8	83.2
sheep	83.9	82.7	92.5	95.8	117.0	76.9
poultry	102.9	159.5	137.0	139.4	134.2	126.4
29 Net value added at basic prices (27 - 28)	107.5	105.1	112.4	112.5	94.8	116.4

source: Defra website, www.defra.gov.uk/esg

(a) Output is net of VAT collected on the sale of non-edible products. Figures for total output include subsidies on products, but not other subsidies.

(b) Includes straw and minor crops.

(c) Landlords' expenses are included within farm maintenance, miscellaneous expenditure and depreciation of buildings and works.

(d) For years prior to 1992 the split between compounds and straights has been estimated based on the split present in later years.

(e) Includes livestock and crop costs, water costs, insurance premiums, bank charges, professional fees, rates, and other farming costs.

(f) A more empirically based methodology for calculating landlords' depreciation was introduced in 2000. The new series has been linked with the old one using a smoothing procedure for the transition year of 1996.

Table 7.2 Productivity

Inquiries: Christine Jeannette on 01904 455080 email: christine.jeannette@defra.gsi.gov.uk

Volume indices 1995=100   Calendar years

Year	Final output (gross output less transaction within the agricultural industry)	Net value added per AWU of all labour (a)	Final output per unit of all inputs (including fixed capital and labour)
1991	101.4	101.3	101.6
1992	101.3	105.4	102.1
1993	98.6	97.2	99.1
1994	99.6	100.9	100.3
1995	100.0	100.0	100.0
1996	99.2	98.1	98.9
1997	99.9	103.3	100.4
1998	100.0	110.0	102.8
1999	101.1	121.8	106.6
2000	97.3	130.0	109.7
2001	91.3	111.2	103.8
2002 (provisional)	96.2	142.0	111.7

source: Defra website, www.defra.gov.uk/esg

(a) An annual work unit (AWU) represents the equivalent of an average
full-time worker engaged in agriculture.

Table 7.3 Costs and volumes of paid labour engaged in agricultural work

Inquiries: Christine Jeannette on 01904 455080 email: christine.jeannette@defra.gsi.gov.uk

Calendar years

	Average of 1991-1993	1998	1999	2000	2001	2002 (provisional)
Paid labour costs (£ million) (a)	1 783	1 977	2 030	1 903	1 909	1 907
Annual work unit ('000) (b)						
Entrepreneurial labour	253	236	229	222	220	212
Paid labour	162	137	132	117	114	109
Total labour force	415	374	361	339	333	321

source: Defra website, www.defra.gov.uk/esg

(a) Includes payments-in-kind to workers, employer and employee
National Insurance contributions, redundancy payments, Workers
Pension Scheme (up to 1990) and the cost of trainees.

(b) An annual work unit (AWU) represents the equivalent of an average
full-time worker engaged in agriculture.

Chapter **8** Subsidies

Introduction | **1** | Chapter 8 gives details of direct subsidies and compensation paid to farmers. Total public expenditure on agriculture under the common agricultural policy (CAP) and other schemes can be found in Chapter 9.

2 Initially, CAP's aims to increase agricultural productivity, safeguard farmers' livelihoods, stabilise markets and guarantee the community's food supply were achieved by market regulation. This was very successful, but also created problems of commodity surpluses and rapidly increasing costs.

3 During the 1970s and 1980s reforms were introduced to curb spending and control over-production by modifying market support measures. The UK launched schemes in 1988 to improve the environment and assist diversification. In 1993 a major reform of the CAP changed the emphasis from supporting prices to direct aid payments to farmers, with consequent savings to consumers from price reductions. The Integrated Administration and Control System (IACS) was introduced for farmers claiming certain subsidies. There was more help for social and environmental measures with the UK introducing schemes to protect, create or improve wildlife habitats and encourage conversion to organic farming.

4 In 2000 the Agenda 2000 reform of the CAP was introduced. The aims were to cut prices and increase direct aid payments to safeguard agricultural incomes, lay the foundations for a comprehensive rural development policy and provide money for environmental schemes.

5 In summary, there are three types of support. Firstly, there is market support in the form of intervention purchases and import tariffs. Market support measures affect the accounts for the agriculture industry through their impact on market prices. Details of the costs to the exchequer can be found in Chapter 9. Secondly, there are direct payments linked to production which form the majority of the present subsidies. Thirdly, there are direct payments linked to rural development.

Direct payments and levies
(Tables 8.1 and 8.2) | **6** | Table 8.1 gives details of the values of the subsidies less levies paid directly to farmers that are included in the income account. Provisional figures show that in 2002 the agricultural industry as a whole received £2.6 billion in direct subsidies less levies, 7.3 per cent more than in 2001. Subsidies related to arable and livestock production rose by 7.7 per cent overall with a larger increase in livestock subsidies compared with arable subsidies. Other payments less levies rose by only 5.8 per cent compared with 109 per cent in 2001.

● Wheat payments were up by £102 million due to an increase in the area cultivated.

● The Over Thirty Month Scheme was £48 million higher and Slaughter Premium

£38 million higher due to recovery after Foot and Mouth Disease.

- Countryside Stewardship payments were £19 million higher.

- Payments for environmental schemes increased by £49 million.

- Set-aside payments were £28 million lower.

Arable Area Payments
(Table 8.3)

7 The Arable Area Payments Scheme (AAPS) is a direct subsidy payable to arable producers. It was introduced in 1993, following the 1992 reform of the CAP, as compensation for reductions in market support. It has developed over the years and was modified as part of the Agenda 2000 reform of the CAP. From 2001 onwards payments are shown after modulation has been applied. No further agrimonetary compensation was payable after 2001.

8 In 2002 total payments made to farmers under AAPS rose by £33 million, or 3.3 per cent, to £1.0 billion. Payments for cereals increased by 13 per cent with a rise of 29 per cent for wheat due to the larger area. The area claimed to set-aside fell by 24 per cent, with payments decreasing by 15 per cent to £152 million. Modulation is estimated to reduce AAPS by £31 million in 2002.

Direct support to livestock producers
(Table 8.4)

9 Five direct subsidies are currently available to livestock producers.

- Beef Special Premium Scheme - a subsidy for male cattle.

- Suckler Cow Premium Scheme - a subsidy on female cattle forming part of a suckler breeding herd used for rearing calves for meat production.

- Extensification Payments Scheme - payments made to farmers who receive Beef Special Premium or the Suckler Cow Premium and meet specific stocking density levels.

- Slaughter Premium Scheme - a subsidy that provides direct support to all producers of domestic cattle.

- Sheep Annual Premium Scheme - a subsidy for breeding ewes.

10 In addition, Member States have additional funds, generally known as National Envelopes. The Beef National Envelope and the Sheep National Envelope can be used to assist beef and sheep producers in ways deemed most appropriate to the structure of the industries. The use made of the National Envelopes can be varied between constituent parts of the UK and from year to year. In England this year, part of the Sheep National Envelope was used to introduce the Sheep Quota Purchase Scheme (SQPS) with the purpose of reducing sheep numbers in areas that have faced historic overgrazing or on land that is of high biodiversity value.

11 There was an increase in the maximum heifer percentage for the Suckler Cow Premium Scheme. From the 2002 scheme year, producers are entitled to claim on heifers in their own right up to a new maximum, which is now 40 per cent of the total number of cattle claimed.

12 In December 2001 changes were adopted to the way subsidies are paid to sheep farmers. These reforms, which came into effect from 1 January 2002, brought in fixed rate premiums based on average pound/euro exchange rates in December (in place of variable premiums linked to average prices on the EU market) for the Sheep Annual Premium Scheme and National Envelopes.

13   Direct support payments to beef producers - Beef Special Premium, Suckler Cow Premium, Extensification Payments, Slaughter Premium, Over Thirty Month Scheme and Beef National Envelope - were affected by Foot and Mouth Disease in 2001. Payments fell by £30 million to £815 million, partly due to the closure of the OTMS for five months. In 2002 payments rose by 13 per cent to £923 million, an increase of 9.2 per cent compared with 2000. Payments under the Sheep Annual Premium Scheme rose by 33 per cent due to the new method for fixing subsidy rates.

14   Overall, provisional figures show that subsidies and other income payments to the livestock sector rose by 8.2 per cent in 2002 to £1.2 billion.

Modulation   15   EU legislation permits Member States to recycle, or modulate, a proportion of payments made direct to farmers under CAP commodity regimes. In order to secure a significant increase in funds for rural development measures all direct payments made under CAP commodity regimes are modulated.

16   Modulation was introduced at a flat rate of 2.5 per cent in the 2001 scheme year to help fund the Rural Development Programme (RDP) through schemes which include Countryside Stewardship, Tir Gofal, Countryside Premium, Environmentally Sensitive Areas and some of the less favoured area schemes. In the 2002 scheme year the rate has been increased to 3 per cent. In other words, 3 per cent of subsidy payments (calculated after taking into account claims, any base reduction and any penalties) will be recycled to help fund the RDP. Under current plans the rate will rise to 4.5 per cent by 2005. Every pound recycled by modulation is matched by a further pound from the government and the total returned through the RDP to the rural economy.

17   On an accruals basis, modulation is estimated to reduce arable and livestock subsidies by around £60 million in 2002.

Agrimonetary compensation   18   The third and final instalment of Transitional Agrimonetary Compensation (TAC) was paid to beef producers to compensate them for the loss of the green rate freeze in 1999. The remaining payments of that compensation package were also made to arable producers. In addition, the payments announced by the government in 2001 to compensate the beef sector for the strength of sterling against the euro were made in 2002. No new payments of agrimonetary compensation were authorised in 2002 and the provisions of EU law allowing the payments of such subsidies have now expired. For accounting reasons, payments made in calendar year 2002 appear in the tables against calendar year 2001.

Capital grants and transfers
(Table 8.5)   19   Capital grants and transfers appear in the capital account as opposed to the income account because they are not related to the activity of production (see also chapter 6, paragraph 28, and table 6.4). Payments under the Sheep Quota Purchase Scheme are included in the capital account as these have been treated as payments for the replacement of capital assets.

Environmental schemes
(Table 8.6)

20 Table 8.6 shows the expenditure on environmental schemes by country. Further details can be found in chapter 10 and areas of land within the various agri-environment schemes are shown in table 10.2.

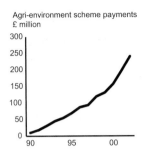

Agri-environment scheme payments
£ million

Table 8.1 Payments and levies in the production and income account

Shows payments after deduction for modulation where appropriate
Inquiries: Christine Jeannette on 01904 455080 email: christine.jeannette@defra.gsi.gov.uk

£ million   Calendar years

	Average of 1991-1993	1998	1999	2000	2001	2002 (provisional)
Subsidies and levies on product (a)						
Crop subsidies						
Arable area payments on:						
wheat	75	466	420	458	351	453
barley	48	277	259	244	260	236
other cereal crops (b)	4	27	25	29	28	33
oilseed rape	51	155	175	110	103	81
linseed	..	48	102	29	10	3
peas and beans - stockfeed and human consumption	37	73	69	59	69	66
other crops	3	6	6	3	7	17
Other crop subsidies (c)	144	16	14	11	2	2
Livestock subsidies:						
Beef Special Premium (d)	83	256	273	216	242	237
Beef Marketing Payment Scheme	..	..	..	..	..	..
Suckler Cow Premium (d)	110	292	255	191	218	218
Slaughter Premium	..	..	..	43	68	106
Extensification Payment Scheme	..	..	..	122	112	128
Calf Processing Aid Scheme	..	52	20	..	..	..
Over Thirty Month Scheme	..	239	266	260	157	205
Hill Livestock Compensatory Allowance - cattle	66	85	87	55	..	..
Beef National Envelope (e)	..	..	..	13	19	29
Sheep Annual Premium	392	395	324	283	186	241
Sheep National Envelope	..	..	..	..	..	7
Hill Livestock Compensatory Allowance - sheep	78	84	86	54	..	..
Foot and Mouth Disease light lambs (f)	..	..	..	..	3	..
Other livestock subsidies (g)	209	..	..	..	..	..
Other subsidies						
Dairy agrimonetary compensation	..	..	..	22	79	..
Levies (h)						
milk superlevy	- 5	- 32	- 9	- 15	..	..
other levies prior to 1994 (i)	- 79	..	..	..	..	..
Total subsidies (less levies) on product	1 076	2 436	2 373	129	1 912	2 060
Other subsidies and levies on production (j)						
Set-aside (k)	142	88	170	127	180	152
Other animal disease compensation (l)	8	24	28	41	28	37
Less favoured areas support schemes (m)	..	..	..	..	168	157

continued

Table 8.1 continued

£ million   Calendar years

	Average of 1991-1993	1998 (a)	1999	2000	2001	2002 (provisional)
Agri-environment schemes:	32	120	131	158	198	247
Countryside Stewardship (n)	7	20	24	30	41	60
Countryside Premium and Rural Stewardship	..	4	7	5	9	9
Tir Cymen and Tir Gofal	..	6	6	8	11	20
Countryside Management Scheme	..	..	..	..	1	1
Organic conversion (o)	..	1	3	19	35	53
Environmentally Sensitive Areas	13	57	59	63	67	70
Nitrate Sensitive Areas	1	6	4	3	2	2
Woodland schemes	5	12	13	16	16	16
Sites of Special Scientific Interest (SSSI) (p)	7	12	13	12	13	13
Energy crops	..	..	..	-	-	-
other (q)	0	3	3	2	4	4
Taxes, including vehicle licences	- 56	- 89	- 90	- 91	- 84	- 76
Other (r)	-	-	..	..	..	..
Total other subsidies and levies on production	31	143	239	235	490	518
Total subsidies less levies	1 107	2 579	2 612	2 422	2 402	2 578

source: Defra website, www.defra.gov.uk/esg

(a) Contribute to basic prices and are included in output in table 6.1.

(b) Oats, rye, mixed corn and triticale.

(c) CAP hops and herbage seeds support, hemp and flax aid, oilseed rape and linseed support and British Potato Council compensation payments.

(d) Includes extensification premium and Northern Ireland deseasonalisation premium.

(e) Payments in England, Wales and Scotland were made to those claiming Suckler Cow Premium. In Northern Ireland, payments were divided between those claiming Slaughter Premium or Suckler Cow Premium.

(f) A 'light lambs' disposal scheme, part of the Livestock Welfare Disposal Scheme. This scheme was introduced to cover lambs that could not be marketed as a result of the ban on exports and restrictions on movement of sheep arising from the outbreak of Foot and Mouth Disease in 2001.

(g) Beef and sheep variable premiums, hill cow, beef cow, calf, hill sheep, pig and calf subsidies.

(h) Excludes levies paid to non-governmental organisations. These are included in the production and income account (table 6.1) under 'other goods and services'.

(i) Wheat, barley, oats, rye, mixed corn and milk co-responsibility levies.

(j) Not included in output but contribute to Net Value Added at factor cost in table 6.1.

(k) Arable Area Payment and former 5-and 1-year schemes.

(l) Tuberculosis, brucellosis, salmonella, Chernobyl, Newcastle and Aujeszky's disease, swine fever and avian influenza compensation and EIC egg scheme.

(m) Land area-based schemes which replaced the Hill Livestock Compensatory Allowance Scheme in 2001. These are Tir Mynydd in Wales, Less Favoured Area Compensatory Allowances Scheme in Northern Ireland, Less Favoured Areas Support Scheme in Scotland and Hill Farm Allowance in England.

(n) Also includes Arable Stewardship.

(o) Includes Organic Aid and Organic Conversion schemes.

(p) Payments for land management for Sites of Special Scientific Interest administered by English Nature, Scottish Natural Heritage and Countryside Council for Wales.

(q) Includes Moorland, Habitat and Countryside Access Farming schemes.

(r) Guidance premium for beef and sheepmeat production, Pilot Beef and Sheep Extensification Scheme and farm accounts grant. Also includes historic data for fertiliser and lime grant and payments to small scale cereal producers.

Table 8.2 Subsidies by country

Shows payments after deduction for modulation where appropriate

Inquiries: Christine Jeannette on 01904 455080 email: christine.jeannette@defra.gsi.gov.uk

£ million   Calendar years

	England 2002	Wales 2002	Scotland 2002	Northern Ireland 2002
Subsidies on product (a)				
Crop subsidies				
Arable area payments on:				
wheat	428.3	2.3	20.6	1.5
barley	157.5	4.5	68.0	5.7
other cereal crops (b)	26.8	0.7	4.9	0.4
oilseed rape	74.5	0.5	5.9	-
linseed	2.6	-	0.1	-
peas and beans - stockfeed and human consumption	63.6	0.5	1.5	0.1
other crops	16.2	0.0	0.1	0.4
Other crop subsidies (c)	0.9	1.2	-	-
Livestock subsidies:				
Beef Special Premium (d)	119.6	26.7	47.1	43.5
Suckler Cow Premium (d)	81.1	35.6	59.4	42.0
Slaughter Premium	59.7	-	19.7	26.6
Extensification Payment Scheme	53.7	-	40.9	33.1
Over Thirty Month Scheme	135.2	-	36.2	33.5
Beef National Envelope (e)	15.2	-	11.2	2.6
Sheep Annual Premium	100.2	61.5	62.0	17.9
Sheep National Envelope	3.3	-	2.7	0.8
Total subsidies on product	1 338.4	133.5	380.2	208.2
Other subsidies on production (f)				
Set-aside (g)	131.8	1.8	17.8	0.6
Less favoured areas support schemes (h)	39.0	31.7	63.0	23.5
Agri-environment schemes:				
Countryside Stewardship (i)	59.5	..	..	..
Countryside Premium and Rural Stewardship	..	..	9.4	..
Tir Cymen and Tir Gofal	..	19.8	..	..
Countryside Management Scheme	..	..	..	1.0
Organic conversion (j)	41.7	2.8	7.1	0.5
Environmentally Sensitive Areas	48.2	7.5	10.2	4.7
Nitrate Sensitive Areas	1.5	..	..	..
Woodland schemes	8.7	0.4	5.3	1.6
Sites of Special Scientific Interest (SSSI) (k)	8.1	2.6	2.5	0.1
Energy crops	0.2	-	-	-
Moorland and Habitat schemes (l)	2.0	1.3	0.4	..
Total other subsidies on production	340.6	67.9	115.6	32.0
Total subsidies	1 678.9	201.4	495.9	240.2

source: Defra website, www.defra.gov.uk/esg

continued

Table 8.2 continued

(a) Contribute to basic prices and are included in output in table 6.1.

(b) Oats, rye, mixed corn and triticale.

(c) CAP hops and herbage seeds support, hemp and flax aid, oilseed rape and linseed support and British Potato Council compensation payments.

(d) Includes extensification premium and Northern Ireland deseasonalisation premium.

(e) Payments in England, Wales and Scotland were made to those claiming Suckler Cow Premium. In Northern Ireland payments were divided between those claiming Slaughter Premium or Suckler Cow Premium.

(f) Not included in output but contribute to Net Value Added at factor cost in table 6.1.

(g) Arable Area Payment and former 5 and 1 year Schemes.

(h) Land area-based schemes which replaced the Hill Livestock Compensatory Allowance Scheme in 2001. These are Tir Mynydd in Wales, Less Favoured Area Compensatory Allowances Scheme in Northern Ireland, Less Favoured Areas Support Scheme in Scotland and Hill Farm Allowance in England.

(i) Also includes Arable Stewardship.

(j) Includes Organic Aid and Organic conversion schemes.

(k) Payments for land management for Sites of Special Scientific Interest administered by English Nature, Scottish Natural Heritage and Countryside Council for Wales.

(l) Includes Moorland, Habitat and Countryside Access Farming schemes.

2002

Table 8.3 Arable Area Payments Scheme (AAPS) and agrimonetary compensation

No new payments of agrimonetary compensation were authorised in 2002

Inquiries: Keith Seabridge on 01904 455081 email: keith.seabridge@defra.gsi.gov.uk

£ million   Calendar years

	1999	2000	2001(c)	2002(c) (provisional)
Wheat	419.7	458.4	350.6	452.8
Arable Area Payments Scheme	361.3	424.5	340.8	452.8
Agrimonetary compensation	58.5	33.9	9.8	..
Barley	259.4	244.3	259.5	235.8
Arable Area Payments Scheme	223.3	224.7	253.7	235.8
Agrimonetary compensation	36.1	19.7	5.8	..
Oats	20.3	23.4	23.3	27.7
Arable Area Payments Scheme	17.5	21.7	22.8	27.7
Agrimonetary compensation	2.8	1.7	0.5	..
Other cereals	5.2	5.5	4.4	5.1
Arable Area Payments Scheme	4.5	5.1	4.3	5.1
Agrimonetary compensation	0.7	0.4	0.1	..
Oilseed Rape	174.9	109.6	103.5	80.9
Arable Area Payments Scheme	150.6	98.2	99.5	80.9
Agrimonetary compensation	24.4	11.4	4.0	..
Linseed	101.9	29.4	10.2	2.7
Arable Area Payments Scheme	87.7	23.9	7.8	2.7
Agrimonetary compensation	14.2	5.5	2.4	..
Peas and beans (a)	68.7	59.2	68.6	65.6
Arable Area Payments Scheme	59.1	54.1	67.0	65.6
Agrimonetary compensation	9.6	5.0	1.6	..
Other crops (b)	5.5	2.7	6.8	16.7
Arable Area Payments Scheme	4.8	2.3	6.7	16.7
Agrimonetary compensation	0.8	0.3	0.1	..
Set-aside	170.0	127.3	179.7	152.0
Arable Area Payments Scheme	146.3	115.5	179.3	152.0
Agrimonetary compensation	23.7	11.8	0.5	..
Total	1 225.7	1 059.8	1 006.7	1 039.4
Arable Area Payments Scheme	1 055.0	970.0	981.9	1 039.4
Agrimonetary compensation	170.7	89.8	24.8	..

source: Defra website, www.defra.gov.uk/esg

(a) Includes total pea crop eligible for Arable Area Payments Scheme (80% assumed for stockfeed and 20% harvested dry for human consumption).

(b) 2001 figures include valuations for flax and hemp crops.

(c) Shows payments after deduction for modulation where appropriate.

Table 8.4 Livestock subsidies and agrimonetary compensation

No new payments of agrimonetary compensation were authorised in 2002

Inquiries: Keith Seabridge on keith.seabridge@defra.gsi.gov.uk. Tel: 01904 455091

£ million   Calendar years

	1997	1998	1999	2000	2001(d)	2002(d) (provisional)
Beef Special Premium Scheme (a) (c)	270.5	256.3	273.2	215.8	241.8	236.9
Beef special premium	270.5	256.3	242.3	197.7	216.2	236.9
Agrimonetary compensation	..	..	31.0	18.1	25.6	..
Suckler Cow Premium Scheme (b) (c)	373.6	291.9	255.0	191.1	218.0	218.1
Suckler cow premium	302.3	244.6	225.8	173.2	194.2	218.1
Agrimonetary compensation	71.2	47.2	29.2	17.9	23.8	..
Sheep Annual Premium Scheme	299.7	394.6	323.8	282.9	186.4	241.5
Sheep annual premium	287.3	363.0	313.7	255.7	166.8	241.5
Agrimonetary compensation	12.4	31.6	10.1	27.2	19.6	..
Extensification Payment Scheme	..	..	..	121.7	112.1	127.6
Extensification payment	..	..	..	117.1	105.3	127.6
Agrimonetary compensation	..	..	..	4.6	6.8	..
Dairy agrimonetary compensation	..	..	..	22.0	79.0	..

source: Defra website, www.defra.gov.uk/esg

(a) Includes Northern Ireland Deseasonalisation Premium and TAC paid to 1999 recipient of the premium.

(b) Includes £50 million BSE Support Payment in 1997, an EU funded package to support the beef industry during the BSE crisis.

(c) Includes extensification payments to 1999 and TAC paid to 1999 recipients, prior to the introduciton of an Extensification Payments Scheme in 2000.

(d) Shows payments after deduction for modulation where appropriate.

Table 8.5 Capital payments

Inquiries: Keith Seabridge on keith.seabridge@defra.gsi.gov.uk. Tel: 01904 455091

£ million   Calendar years

	1995	1996	1997	1998	1999	2000	2001	2002 (provisional)
BSE - animal disease (from 1988)	11.1	7.0	4.6	19.9	10.4	3.1	13.7	0.2
BSE - selective cull (from 1997)	..	..	78.1	42.7	2.3	-	..	..
Scrapie (from 1998)	..	..	..	11.4	5.3	-	10.1	-
Sheep National Envelope - Quota purchase	..	..	..	..	..	..	-	2.0
Pig Welfare Disposal Scheme	..	..	..	..	..	8.7	3.9	..
Pig Industry Restructuring Scheme	..	..	..	..	..	..	46.9	21.7
Foot and Mouth Disease (a)	..	..	..	..	..	..	1 313.4	..
Non-marketing of milk (1980 - 1986)	..	..	..	..	..	..	..	..
Milk outgoers (1984 - 1994)	..	..	..	..	..	..	..	..
Milk quota cuts (1987 - 1997)	26.0	26.1	26.9	..	..	..	..	..
Capital grants (b)	13.6	10.1	8.2	8.7	7.0	7.2	7.8	8.0

source: Defra Statistics website, www.defra.gov.uk/esg

(a) For full breakdown see table 6.4

(b) Includes farm diversity, farm and conservation, agriculture improvement scheme, agriculture and horticulture and farm structures grants.

Table 8.6 Environmental scheme payments by country

Inquiries: Christine Jeannette on 01904 455080 email: christine.jeannette@defra.gsi.gov.uk

£ million   Scheme years

	1993	1994	1995	1996	1997	1998	1999	2000	2001	2002 (provisional)
Total expenditure	44.3	53.4	67.2	84.4	91.2	116.8	127.9	154.2	198.2	245.7
England										
Environmentally Sensitive Areas	16.2	19.3	24.3	26.8	28.6	37.6	39.5	40.9	42.0	48.2
Countryside Stewardship	8.5	10.5	11.6	10.9	15.7	19.9	23.4	28.9	39.6	58.0
Arable Stewardship	..	..	..	..	..	..	0.5	0.9	1.3	1.5
Organic Conversion	..	..	0.1	0.3	0.7	1.2	2.3	15.4	26.5	41.7
Nitrate Sensitive Areas	1.6	3.6	4.1	4.7	4.7	6.2	3.9	2.6	1.7	1.5
Countryside Access	..	..	0.1	0.1	0.1	0.1	0.1	-	-	-
Habitat scheme	..	..	1.0	1.4	1.8	1.8	1.9	1.9	2.0	1.9
Moorland scheme	..	..	..	0.1	0.2	0.2	0.2	0.2	0.1	0.1
Woodland schemes	2.2	2.9	3.4	3.8	4.7	5.4	5.9	6.0	7.6	8.7
Energy crops	..	..	..	..	..	..	..	0.2	0.2	0.2
English Nature, SSSI (a)	7.6	6.6	6.6	6.1	6.3	6.2	7.8	7.6	7.7	8.1
Wales										
Environmentally Sensitive Areas	..	..	1.5	2.4	3.3	5.4	6.2	6.7	7.1	7.5
Tir Cymen	..	2.9	3.4	4.9	5.2	5.5	5.7	5.5	5.1	4.4
Tir Gofal	..	..	..	..	..	..	..	2.2	8.9	15.4
Organic Conversion	..	..	..	..	..	..	..	..	3.3	2.8
Habitat scheme	..	..	..	..	..	..	..	..	0.7	0.7
Moorland scheme	..	..	..	..	..	..	..	..	0.6	0.6
Woodland schemes	3.3	..	0.1	0.2	0.2	0.2	0.2	0.3	0.3	0.4
Countryside Council for Wales, SSSI (a)	..	1.8	1.9	2.6	2.5	3.0	2.7	2.3	2.4	2.6
Scotland										
Environmentally Sensitive Areas	1.0	1.0	2.0	3.4	5.2	7.5	7.1	9.5	11.0	10.2
Countryside Premium	1.0	1.2	2.1	2.4	0.4	3.7	6.9	5.0	8.5	6.1
Rural Stewardship	..	..	..	..	..	..	..	..	..	3.3
Organic Conversion	..	..	..	..	0.1	0.2	0.4	2.9	4.6	7.1
Habitat and moorland schemes	0.6	0.6	1.1	4.0	0.4	0.5	0.4	0.3	0.4	0.4
Woodland schemes	1.7	2.2	2.6	2.9	2.8	3.3	3.8	4.3	4.0	5.3
Scottish natural heritage, SSSI (a)	..	..	..	3.2	2.5	2.4	2.2	2.2	2.3	2.5
Northern Ireland										
Environmentally Sensitive Areas	0.6	0.6	1.1	4.0	5.6	6.1	6.2	6.0	7.4	4.7
Organic Conversion	..	..	..	..	..	..	..	0.4	0.4	1.6
Woodland schemes	0.2	0.2	0.2	0.2	0.3	0.4	0.6	2.0	1.5	1.6
Countryside Management Scheme	..	..	..	..	..	..	..	..	0.9	1.0
ASSI (a)	..	..	..	..	..	0.3	0.5	0.1	0.1	0.1

source: Defra website, www.defra.gov.uk/esg

(a) Sites of Special Scientific Interest (SSSI) or Areas of Special
Scientific Interest (ASSI) that are managed under Environmentally
Sensitive Areas (ESA) or stewardship schemes are not also
included in SSSI or ASSI.

Chapter 9 Public expenditure on agriculture

Introduction
1 Table 9.1 shows public expenditure under the Common Agricultural Policy (CAP) and on national grants and subsidies. The table does not include other expenditure of benefit to farmers and the farming community such as expenditure on animal health, research, advice and education.

2 The figures for the financial year 2001/02 represent actual expenditure recorded in the Rural Payments Agency (RPA) resource account for the year ended 31 March 2002 combined with actual expenditure figures for the national agriculture departments. The figures for 2002/03 are the latest estimates of expenditure. From 2001/02 accrual accounting has been used and the figures reported are based on these accrual accounts. This accounting change means that directly comparable historical figures cannot be provided as cash figures were previously used for the table.

Chart 9.1 Public expenditure under CAP

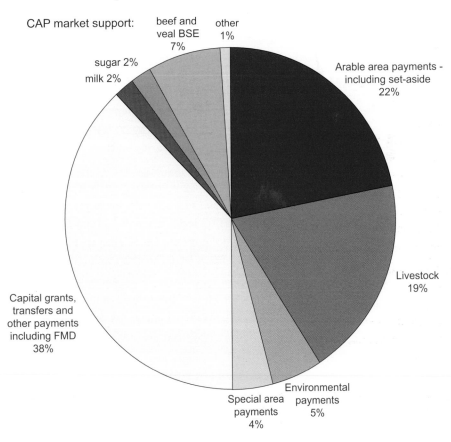

3 The RPA was established in October 2001 as an executive agency of Defra. It is an accredited EU paying agency responsible for CAP schemes in England and for the administration of certain schemes throughout the UK. The RPA is also the UK funding body responsible for receiving and accounting for payment of all CAP guarantee funds, including those made by devolved administrations. Defra retains overall responsibility for all policy matters relating to the CAP.

4   The Scottish Executive, National Assembly for Wales and Department of Agriculture and Rural Development retain responsibilities for other schemes within Scotland, Wales and Northern Ireland respectively.

Public expenditure
(Table 9.1)

5   Total expenditure in 2001/02 was £4.7 billion compared with £3.0 billion in 2000/01. The increase in 2001/02 was mainly attributable to the impact of the Foot and Mouth Disease outbreak in 2001. Expenditure in 2002/03 is forecast at £3.1 billion.

6   Under the CAP, direct subsidies for arable and livestock production during 2001/02 were £1.9 billion. Market support measures were £555 million, including £307 million expenditure on the Over Thirty Months Scheme (OTMS). (OTMS is a measure introduced as a public health measure in response to BSE and to give aid to farmers and is co-financed by the EU). Net expenditure on rural, conservation and agri-environment schemes was £214 million.

7   In 2001/02 other payments amounting to £1.8 billion related principally to Foot and Mouth Disease compensation payments and disposal schemes.

8   Forecasts for expenditure in 2002/03 suggest that the overall Arable Area Payments Scheme will not change significantly from 2001/02. However, within this total, expenditure on cereals is forecast to increase while expenditure on oilseeds and set-aside is forecast to fall. Expenditure on rural, conservation and agri-environment schemes is forecast to increase. The Foot and Mouth Disease restrictions impacted on the number of OTMS presentations in 2001/02. In 2002/03 expenditure on this scheme is expected to rise by 30 per cent to reach similar levels to those before the Foot and Mouth Disease outbreak.

Modulation

6   Modulation money is not necessarily spent in the year of modulation, but if it is not spent by the end of the third scheme year following modulation it is refunded to the EU. In 2001/02 modulation deductions totalled £31 million of which £9 million (matched by equivalent UK Exchequer funding) was used to fund rural development measures. The balance of £22.1 million was retained for use in future years.

7   Expenditure on schemes subject to modulation is shown in table 9.1 gross of modulation. Where payments are made out of modulation funds on rural development measures, the modulation funds are applied as income against total expenditure.

Table 9.1 Public expenditure under CAP and on national grants and subsidies

Inquiries: Rural Payments Agency on 0118 953 1725 email: ian.thomas@rpa.gsi.gov.uk

£ million (a)	actual 2001/02	forecast 2002/03
A. Total direct product subsidies	1 888.2	1 922.7
Arable Area Payments Scheme	1 015.5	1 037.3
cereals	648.7	737.3
oilseeds	109.7	85.8
other	66.6	66.6
set-aside	186.9	147.1
agrimonetary compensation	3.6	0.5
of which EU funded (%)	100%	100%
Livestock subsidies	870.8	885.4
cattle and calves	650.9	688.3
sheep	166.7	191.9
agrimonetary compensation	51.6	4.8
of which EU funded (%)	100%	100%
Additional agrimonetary compensation (DARD)	1.6	0.4
Milk (b)	1.9	. .
of which EU funded (%)	100%	100%
B. Total other subsidies on production	392.6	484.5
Total rural, conservation,agri-environment (c)	214.4	294.5
agri-environment and conservation schemes	210.5	264.9
rural schemes	3.9	29.6
Total special area support (d)	175.6	187.9
less favoured areas: remnant schemes	20.9	24.7
less favoured area: current schemes	154.7	163.2
Total animal disease	2.6	2.0
of which EU funded (%)	0%	0%
C: Total capital grants, transfers and other payments	1 828.0	11.6
Total diversification and capital grants	6.5	9.8
Total animal disease (e)	1 819.9	1.1
FMD compensation payments	1 116.4	-
FMD welfare disposal schemes (f)	37.0	-
FMD cleansing, disinfecting and disposal costs	666.1	0.4
other	0.4	0.7
Total other (structural and guidance)	1.6	0.7
D: Total CAP market support	555.1	700.4
Cereals	4.8	8.7
of which EU funded (%)	100%	100%
Sugar	106.0	94.8
of which EU funded (%)	100%	100%
Milk products	83.1	142.1
of which EU funded (%)	95%	95%
Processed goods	28.3	28.7
of which EU funded (%)	100%	100%

continued

Table 9.1 continued

£ million (a)

	actual 2001/02	forecast 2002/03
Total beef and veal (BSE)	114.4	145.6
BSE (disposal)	114.4	126.2
TSE surveillance (g)	-	19.4
of which EU funded (%)	0%	0%
Beef and veal (BSE compensation)	192.3	253.7
of which EU funded (%)	70%	70%
Beef and veal (non-BSE)	0.5	1.0
of which EU funded (%)	100%	100%
Sheepmeat	0.1	-
of which EU funded (%)	100%	100%
Pigmeat	4.1	4.1
of which EU funded (%)	100%	100%
Others (h)	21.4	21.7
of which EU funded (%)	100%	100%
Total public expenditure (A + B + C + D)	4 663.9	3 119.2

source: RPA and Defra

(a) The figures are net of receipts which are treated as negative expenditure.

(b) Dairy agrimonetary compensation was paid during 2001/02 but was accrued back to the previous year (2000/01) and therefore is not shown in this table.

(c) These schemes are partly EU funded. Funding varies from 35 to 50 per cent depending on the national contribution to the scheme.

(d) These schemes are partly EU funded. Funding varies from 15 to 20 per cent depending on the national contribution to the scheme.

(e) These schemes are partly EU funded. The level of funding for Foot and Mouth Disease payments is not available.

(f) Actual cash expenditure on RPA-administered Foot and Mouth Disease welfare disposal schemes in 2001/02 was £331m but this was mainly paid out of provisions made under the 2000/01 resource budget.

(g) TSE - Transmissible Spongiform Encephalopathies.

(h) Includes fish, fresh fruit and vegetables, hops, protein and textile plants, seeds, wine, eggs and poultry.

Chapter **10** Environment

Introduction **1** Environmental accounts are compiled by the Office for National Statistics for the United Kingdom as a whole and are being developed. They are satellite accounts to the main National Accounts. They provide information on the environmental impact of economic activity and on the importance of natural resources to the economy. Environmental accounts use similar concepts and classifications of industries to those employed in the National Accounts, and they reflect the recommended European Union and United Nations frameworks for developing such accounts. The statistics shown in this chapter are intended to fit in with this framework.

2 Traditional farming methods together with climatic conditions and the underlying geology have produced distinctive regional landscapes. Local building materials, species of vegetation and management practices give rise to characteristic buildings and field boundaries with walls produced from local stone and local species in hedges or ditches. These contribute to the diverse nature of the UK countryside and the unique character areas (such as the Countryside Agency character/natural areas). This variety provides a range of habitats for native flora and fauna. These unique agri-ecosystems and their biodiversity can be conserved, enhanced or damaged by farming methods.

3 The agricultural sector in the UK is made up of around 230 thousand holdings. These vary widely in size and type and employ a range of different farming practices. The way in which livestock are kept; the use of inputs; soil, water, waste, nutrient and land management (as well as local environmental characteristics) affect the extent to which farming activities impact on the environment. The effects of agriculture on the environment are therefore significant and complex - farming activities can give rise to both positive and negative impacts operating at local, regional, national and global levels. Where farming activities are carried out in an environmentally responsible manner, positive impacts include supporting and maintaining a range of diverse landscapes and providing a range of habitats and food sources for farmland wildlife. Negative impacts include the polluting effects of pesticides and fertilisers and emissions of CO_2 and other greenhouse gases. Some environmental impacts are interrelated; for example poor land management leads to soil erosion, which in turn leads to water pollution.

4 Over time, technical developments in farming - and incentives that are embedded within the mechanisms of the Common Agriculture Policy (CAP) - have often tended to result in adverse environmental trends. The environmental benefits that were once the result of traditional farming practices (and hence were delivered without government intervention) have been reduced by developments in modern farming methods (e.g. the need for larger field sizes to operate modern machinery and the switch from spring- to autumn-sown cereals) or by policy incentives (e.g. livestock headage payments tending to encourage overgrazing with damaging impacts particularly in fragile upland ecosystems).

Environmental impacts

Landscape, habitats and biodiversity
(Chart 10.1)

5 Agriculture accounts for around three-quarters of land cover and produces two-thirds of our food in the UK. It has a large environmental impact upon the rural landscape and (through their use) on natural resources. Agriculture is responsible for the appearance of much of the landscape, for the conservation, provision and protection of farmland wildlife habitats, for maintaining water and soil resources, protecting natural and historical features as well as playing an important role in flood prevention.

6 Land management supports and maintains diverse landscapes. The value of regionally distinctive landscapes associated with each region's traditional farming system is well recognised (e.g. Pretty et al, 2000; Hartridge and Pearce, 2001; Environment Agency, 2002; Willis et al, 1993; Hanley, 2001; McInerney et al, 2000). This is reflected in the many people visiting the countryside for recreational activities. The extent to which the public can benefit from such traditional rural landscapes depends partly on their having access to agricultural land through a network of public rights of way and open access land.

7 Chart 10.1 shows the extent of public concern over various environmental issues. There is widespread concern about the environment, with issues relating to agriculture of as much concern as those in other areas of the environment. Nearly 60 per cent of the population are concerned about the effects of livestock methods

Chart 10.1 Concern about environmental issues: 2001

ENGLAND

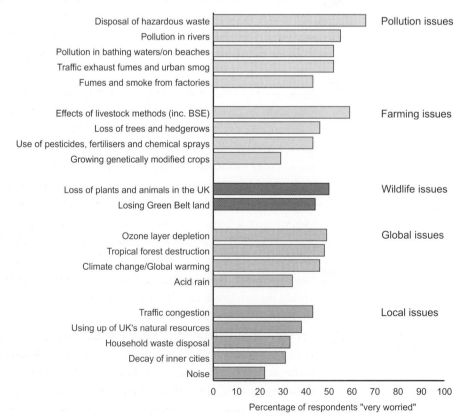

Percentage of respondents "very worried"

Source: Defra, 2003

while over half the population are concerned about pollution in rivers.

8   Agricultural practices continue to shape the countryside. Agriculture provides access and opportunities for recreational activities and has the potential to protect historic and other features. This could be seen as a major positive impact. Without agriculture the countryside would be very different, but would still provide habitats for plants and animals. Although not easy to quantify, agriculture contributes significantly to the rural, social and economic infrastructure, in particular indirectly through the environment it creates for tourism (Countryside Agency, 2001), recreation, marketing industries and, arguably, rural industry more widely.

9   Some negative environmental impacts are clearly the result of poor farming practices. Others may be difficult to avoid in intensive production systems even where farmers are behaving responsibly, and could only be reduced with significant changes to the make-up of a farm's productive activities (e.g. switching to organic production; taking land out of intensive livestock production). Many of the negative impacts are already controlled through existing regulation, voluntary initiatives or other measures.

10   In some areas, farming activities have helped to conserve semi-natural habitats and wildlife. However, intensification of agriculture has often led to the loss of habitats and the erosion of landscape character. The condition of Sites of Special Scientific Interest (SSSI) habitats are being assessed, with the number of inspections increasing each year. Between 2000 and 2002 about 55 to 60 per cent were in a favourable condition (Defra, 2002(a)).

11   Agriculture creates and conserves a complex range of habitats and food sources for farmland wildlife. Much of our flora and fauna have adapted to agricultural systems and the common names of wild species indicate their historic relationship with farming, such as corncrake, corn cockle, cornflower and corn marigold.

12   According to Pretty et al (2000), species diversity is declining, including in the farmed habitat itself. Draining and fertilisers have replaced flower-rich meadows with grass monocultures and contributed to the loss or degradation of characteristic hedgerow and field margin vegetation. Overgrazing of uplands and the abandonment or under-management of semi-natural infield habitats - mostly in the lowlands - have reduced species diversity. Herbicides have reduced species diversity in arable fields. Farmland birds have particularly suffered, mainly as a result of a shift from spring-sown to autumn-sown cereals. The populations of nine species fell by more than a half between 1970 and 1995 (Pretty et al, 2000). Cropping systems have become simplified and more specialised with a loss of crop rotations and arable-pasture mosaics, resulting in a lower diversity of habitats and a severe reduction in characteristic farmland species.

Resources
(Table 10.1)

13   Soil is a limited resource that is essential for plant growth. The biological, physical and chemical characteristics need to be maintained. It also provides a habitat for earthworms and other fauna, which are essential for the soil structure and play their part in the wild life food chain. Agricultural practices have an important part to play in protecting and improving the soil and preventing its loss by erosion. The careful management of soil is essential for all farming so that it remains a renewable

resource. Rates of soil erosion from agricultural land are generally significant and are high where sensitive soil systems are managed inappropriately. The Environment Agency (2002) suggests that agriculture contributes 95 per cent to soil erosion overall. Soil erosion may lead to falling soil productivity through soil losses and plant damage, as well as increased fertiliser and sowing costs.

14   Water is a renewable resource so long as over-extraction does not have a permanent effect on the level of the water table, particularly during times of drought, and it is not polluted with agricultural waste. Excessive water abstraction has damaged some wetland habitats by lowering the water table. The benefits of water accumulation and supply, nutrient recycling and fixation, soil formation as well as flood control are recognised (e.g. Pretty et al, 2000; Environment Agency, 2002).

15   Changes in agricultural land use and cultivation practices are increasing rainwater run-off and contributing to flooding. River catchment surveys in winter 2000 revealed widespread damage to soil structure, with 50 per cent of soils having damaged structure in one area. Modelled predictions suggested potential increase in run-off from 1.2 per cent to 20 per cent for an individual storm.

16   Resources can be renewable (sustainable) or non-renewable (using up finite resources). Some finite resources are consumed by the agricultural industry and are used in the form of petroleum, coal and gas and in production of electricity. They are also used in the form of metals in the manufacture of equipment and in the form of chemicals in fertilisers and pesticides.

17   The data available on consumption of finite resources are represented by statistics on direct and indirect energy consumption. Table 10.1 shows estimated direct and indirect use converted into PetaJoules - Joules x 10^{15} (PJ) for purposes of comparison. This is the energy consumed in agricultural production and not in the manufacture and distribution of food.

18   Energy used directly by the agricultural industry represented 0.3 per cent of overall UK energy consumption in the year 2001.

19   Energy use in agriculture can be classified into:

●   direct use of energy (including electricity) for heating and motive power;

●   indirect input from the manufacture of fertilisers, pesticides and machinery.

20   The direct energy data in table 10.1 is provided on an 'as supplied to agriculture' basis. Energy supplied does not include the efficiency of generation and losses in handling and refining. Although direct energy use in agriculture increased by 0.6 per cent in 2001 compared to 2000, it has declined slowly during the last 16 years by 18 per cent with the reduction of housed livestock. The development of new and enhanced sustainable farming technologies, such as minimum tillage, should help the sector further improve its energy efficiency. However, changes are dependant to some extent on factors that are outside the sector's control - most notably the weather.

21   The most dominant indirect input of energy arises from the manufacture of

2002

fertilisers. Reductions in the use of fertilisers and pesticides are reflected in a decline of energy use between 1985 and 2000 of the energy used in their manufacture of 20 and 23 per cent respectively. The use of fertilisers in 2001 dropped a further 12 per cent whilst pesticide use increased slightly by 5 per cent. Despite this increase, the long-term trend since 1985 has been downwards. The adoption of organic production methods gives further scope for reduction.

22 Agriculture plays an important role in renewable energy. Conversion technologies are aimed at two levels, small scale on-farm combustion for heat production and electricity generation for sale under the Non-fossil Fuel Obligation and the Renewables Obligation. Table 10.1 shows the level of direct use of biomass by agriculture.

23 Biofuels produced by agriculture will contribute to the policy to generate 10 per cent of national electricity by 2010 from renewable resources. Renewable-energy power station developments in the UK since 1992 include the world's first four poultry litter power stations and the world's largest straw-fired power station. These have a combined generating capacity of 111 MWe (MegaWatts electrical). In addition, there are smaller stations operating on wood fuel.

24 The first large-scale anaerobic digestion plant in the UK has now started operation. The plant has a generator capacity of 2.1 MWe and processes cattle, pig, poultry and food process organic waste.

25 Agricultural biomass and farm waste account for 15 per cent of the inputs for the generation of renewable energy in the UK. The quantity of renewable energy production from agricultural sources rose by 23 per cent to 20PJ (478 thousand tonnes of oil equivalent). This equates to 40 per cent of the direct energy consumption used in agricultural production.

Emissions and pollution
(Chart 10.2)

26 Agricultural and forestry activity contributes to global emissions of three of the six greenhouse gases identified in the Kyoto Protocol, namely carbon dioxide (CO_2), methane (CH_4) and nitrous oxide (N_2O). CO_2 is emitted during cultivation of arable land or semi-natural vegetation when the soil is rotated to the surface and exposed to the air; when peat or fenland is drained; and during the combustion of fossil fuels to power tractors and machinery (Hartridge and Pearce, 2001). All plant growth, including grass, crops and trees, takes in carbon from CO_2 and releases oxygen. This makes vegetation a short-term carbon sink, in which carbon is tied up from one to several hundred years before being re-released. The use of fossil fuels releases carbon from sinks formed millions of years ago. This cannot be balanced with the carbon taken up in current plant growth which is part of a far shorter carbon cycle.

27 Chart 10.2 shows methane emissions in the UK by source, including those from agriculture (which have remained fairly constant at a million tonnes per year). Methane is formed from decomposition of animal wastes and fermentation in the intestines of livestock. Agriculture is estimated to be the largest source of methane gas in the UK.

28 Nitrous oxide is formed from nitrogen fertilisers and from the treatment and

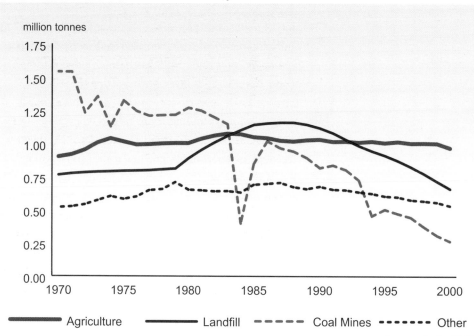

Chart 10.2 Methane emissions by source 1970-2000

Source: Defra 2003

disposal of animal wastes. Hartridge and Pearce (2001) cite agriculture as the largest source of nitrous oxide in the UK.

29 It is difficult to collate data on total emissions and pollution from agriculture as they come from diffuse and hugely variable sources often resulting in insufficient data being available. For fertiliser and pesticide losses, data are based on samples of river and ground water that do not give a full or continuous picture of losses. Nor do they show whether pesticides break down rapidly or persist in the environment.

30 There are emissions of ammonia (NH_3) to the air, contributing to problems of acidification and eutrophication. Currently 85 per cent of the ammonia entering the atmosphere in the UK is from fertilisers and manures used in agriculture. Ammonia may also lead to acidification of soils and waters in the uplands, especially in areas receiving heavy atmospheric pollution. Acidification leads to loss of aquatic biodiversity, such as reduced populations of freshwater fish. Livestock farming contributed 85 per cent of the UK's ammonia emissions to air in 1999.

31 Agriculture is the largest user of pesticides (89 per cent, Environment Agency, 2002) which include herbicides, fungicides and insecticides used to protect crops and plantations from competing species, pests and diseases. Pesticides dispersed in the air or received in soils may have adverse impacts on ecosystems. They may affect the availability of food sources for birds by eliminating invertebrates and destroying the habitat of species upon which birds prey. There may also be human health impacts (from residues in food, exposure to spray drift, operator use, etc.). The on-farm costs associated with pesticides include human and domestic animal health issues, pesticide resistance and crop losses.

32 Pesticides can cause water pollution, entering surface waters by spillage, spray drift and run-off, and leaching into ground waters. They are likely to have toxic effects on aquatic plants or animals, and they may also exceed the permitted limit for

pesticides in drinking water, increasing drinking water treatment costs.

33 Veterinary medicines, including pesticides such as sheep dip, antibiotics, hormones, growth regulators and disinfectants are also a possible source of water pollution although less is known about their risks to wildlife.

34 Inorganic fertilisers, manure and slurry are used to increase the nutrient content of soil and promote crop growth. The nutrients, nitrates and phosphates contained in fertilisers can lead to water pollution through run-off and leaching.

35 The Environment Agency recently estimated that agriculture is responsible for 43 per cent of phosphate in surface water, 29 per cent coming from livestock and 14 per cent from fertilisers. Many lakes and rivers in the UK are heavily enriched with both nitrogen and phosphorus. Thus enriched waters put wetlands fed by these waters at risk, as well as aquatic Special Sites of Scientific Interest (SSSI). A report by Carvalho and Moss in 1998 concluded that 80 of 95 lakes and other standing water SSSIs surveyed in England were suffering from eutrophication (English Nature 2002).

36 Intensification of farming practices in the last twenty years has resulted in a vast increase in the quantity of manure and slurry produced. Run-off from land spread with manure or slurry, or from areas used for keeping livestock, contains pathogens (bacteria, protozoa, viruses) present in animal faeces, heavy metals and ammonium compounds produced by the decomposition of organic material. The environmental damage can be significant. The organic content of run-off can lead to high organic loads in streams, ponds, lakes and ditches. This has adverse impacts on aquatic ecosystems and leads to increased drinking water treatment costs and monitoring expenditure as well as limiting access to recreational waters.

37 There is a range of small point sources on farms, for example failure of manure, silage and slurry stores; farmyard or farm track run-off where there are inadequate dirty water collection and drainage systems. Such sources are a frequent cause of acute water pollution problems. Yard washings and slurry accounted for more than half of the 2,063 substantiated water pollution incidents involving organic materials in 2000.

38 At present approximately two-thirds of all farm wastes are burnt in the open air or buried. Uncontrolled burning can lead to potentially hazardous emissions to air and soil, including dioxins. Burning of hazardous wastes can also cause long-term pollution and soil contamination. In 2000 agricultural waste accounted for 20 per cent of UK waste (Defra 2003).

Economic valuations of environmental impacts

39 Economic valuations of both positive and negative impacts from recent studies are referred to as a guide to the overall significance of those impacts. Because there are often no markets, and therefore no prices for environmental goods (e.g. clean air, visual amenity and biodiversity), it is not usually possible to obtain economic values

for environmental impacts using market prices. Values must therefore be inferred or estimated using a range of techniques which fall into two main categories.

40 Some techniques measure the impact of environmental problems on the well-being of humans (welfare impacts) by estimating society's readiness to pay to secure an improvement or avoid a reduction in environmental quality. These techniques either elicit values directly from people (through surveys) or indirectly by observing actual behaviour in related markets (for example, house prices in areas affected by environmental problems can be compared with similar properties in areas free of such problems).

41 Other techniques look for surrogate measures of welfare impacts using goods that do have market prices (surrogate costs). For example, pollution control costs are used as a measure of the value that society places on reducing pollution. This is based on the assumption that if society has chosen to reduce pollution, it must have been willing to pay at least the pollution control costs (or more) to reduce that pollution. The pollution control costs therefore provide an estimate of society's value for reducing pollution. Such techniques are usually used in the absence of estimates of willingness to pay - they do not represent the true value of welfare impacts, only a proximate value.

42 Where a change in environmental quality has a positive or negative impact on production costs or income, the change in costs or income can usually be measured using market prices. The production costs approach is useful in demonstrating the resource implications of environmental problems, whereas the welfare impacts approach demonstrates how important an environmental impact is to society as a whole. They measure different things, and one should not expect the values they produce to be similar. They can both contribute to measuring the 'Total Economic Value' of an environmental resource.

43 Valuation techniques for an environmental impact usually provide a range of values, taking into account the uncertainty inherent in estimating values. Further sources of uncertainty include quantifying environmental impacts and the extent to which agricultural activities give rise to those impacts. Estimates of the value of the environmental impacts of agriculture that are provided below should be treated with a great deal of care. They are provided as a guide to the significance of different environmental effects rather than as a statement of their absolute magnitude. Uncertainty and omitted impacts (impacts that have not been valued) mean that one should not draw conclusions by comparing the totals for the estimates of costs and benefits. Alternative land uses would also produce a range of positive and negative environmental impacts. These are not available for comparison and are not necessary to demonstrate the significance of the different environmental impacts of agriculture.

44 A recent study by Hartridge and Pearce (2001) estimated the value of a (not exhaustive) range of positive environmental impacts of agriculture at around £595 million per year (see table below). The Environment Agency (2002) adjust this figure to include the benefits of carbon sinks and estimate total benefits at around £914 million per year (2000 prices). Although there are large uncertainties surrounding these valuations, there is evidence (Willis et al, 1993; Stewart et al,

1997; Hanley, 2001) that society values the diversity of agricultural landscapes (with their associated wildlife habitats and biodiversity impacts), and that these are currently under-provided.

45 The results of three recent studies, which attempt to value the cost of agriculture's negative environmental impacts, are summarised in the second table. Only those negative environmental impacts of agriculture that can be quantified and for which economic values have already been established are included. The figures are not directly comparable because the studies from which the figures are derived cover slightly different sets of impacts and value different things (e.g. welfare impacts versus production costs).

46 The study by Hartridge and Pearce (2001) seeks to estimate the environmental costs of UK agriculture, mainly using values from a range of willingness to pay studies (the welfare impacts approach) both from the UK and abroad. The authors estimate the depreciation of the stock of natural capital associated with agriculture and the environmental services generated. They obtain the relevant values from willingness to pay estimates to arrive at cost estimates.

47 The study by Pretty et al (2000) estimates the environmental costs of UK agriculture mainly by examining the expenditure which society incurs in dealing with it (the production costs approach).

48 The study by the Environment Agency (2002) draws on these two earlier studies but includes, in particular, more extensive work on soil erosion. It should be noted that the study does not attempt to include costs associated with damage to biodiversity, landscapes or to human health.

49 Further information on the positive and negative impacts of agriculture on the environment can be found in Defra (2002b).

Economic values of positive environmental impacts of agriculture

Environmental Services	£ million per year (1998 prices)
Agricultural Landscape	140.7
Forest and Woodland	84.5
Environmentally Sensitive Areas	187.6
Sites of Special Scientific Interest (a)	182.1
Total (b)	594.9

Source: Hartridge and Pearce (2001)

Care should be taken with these figures as they are very broad and uncertain and based on one study.

(a) This figure includes the valuation of the Countryside Stewardship Scheme, Organic Farming Scheme, habitat scheme, and Nitrate Sensitive Areas.

(b) Adjusting this value to include the benefits of carbon sinks gives a total of £955.5 million per year.

Economic values of negative environmental impacts of agriculture
£ million per year

Environmental impacts	Value		
	Hartridge and Pearce (1998 prices)	Pretty et al (1996 prices)	Environment Agency (2000 prices)
Damage to natural capital:			
Water	428	231	203
Air	585	1,113	760
Soil	21	96	264
Biodiversity and landscape	38	126	
Total (a)	1,072	1,566	1,227

Source: Hartridge and Pearce, 2001; Pretty et al, 2000; Environment Agency 2002

(a) Adjusting this value to exclude the benefits of carbon sinks gives a total of £1,433 million per year.

Environmental indicators and targets

50   Sustainability indicators are being developed by a number of organisations for the economic, social and environmental aspects of agriculture. The Organisation for Economic Co-operation and Development (OECD) is working on agri-environment indicators that will give policy makers a better understanding of the environmental impacts of agriculture.

51   Eurostat is developing a set of 35 agri-environment indicators to monitor the state and trend of agriculture's impact on the landscape including indicators for farm practices; water use and pollution; soil erosion and nutrient balance; pesticide use and residue; energy use; land cover and land use; habitat, genetic and species diversity; industrial crops; greenhouse emissions and landscape state and change.

52   The Scottish Executive Environment and Rural Affairs Department (SEERAD) is, in conjunction with stakeholders, developing a series of indicators that will help measure, in environmental, economic and social terms, the success of its Agriculture Strategy, which was published in 2001.

53   Defra is developing a series of headline and core indicators to monitor and evaluate its strategy for sustainable farming and food. One target is to achieve favourable conditions on 95 per cent of SSSIs by 2010. Defra plans to publish regular reports on the progress of the strategy with details of indicators and targets.

54   Bird populations are considered good indicators of the state of wildlife in the countryside since they have a wide habitat distribution and are near the top of the food chain. Therefore, they reflect changes in habitat diversity and in the food chain. Chart 10.3 shows that total farmland bird populations declined by almost half between 1978 and 1993, but have been relatively stable since. This decline reflects the drop in farmland specialist birds by 60 per cent.

55   The UK Biodiversity Action Plan includes targets to reverse the decline in wild bird populations to preserve natural diversity. Targets include reversing the decline in breeding and over-wintering numbers and also increasing their range and habitats.

Chart 10.3 Key bird populations

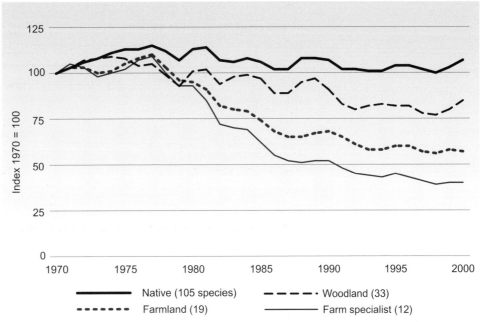

Native (105 species)   Woodland (33)
Farmland (19)   Farm specialist (12)

Surveys of bird populations have been carried out by the British Trust for Ornithology (BTO) and Royal Society for the Protection of Birds (RSPB). Data for 2001 is unavailable because of Foot and Mouth Disease restrictions during that year.

Land designation and management

56 There is a range of designated areas in the UK which give various measures of protection for a variety of reasons. Many of the designated areas incorporate land management practices for conservation, biodiversity and other environmental benefits. They can be designated by national or local governments and are not mutually exclusive; Sites of Special Scientific Interest (SSSI) or nature reserves can be within Areas of Outstanding Natural Beauty (AONBs) or national parks.

57 The national parks were designated in England and Wales in the 1950s. The 10 parks cover an area of over 14 thousand km², nearly 8 per cent of the land area in England and 20 per cent in Wales. A further two parks are proposed in England. Scotland's first national park was Loch Lomond and the Trossachs (2002), covering an area of 1,865 km²; the Cairngorms will become a national park during 2003. The main aims are to conserve and enhance the natural beauty, wildlife and cultural heritage; promote public understanding and enjoyment of the special qualities of the area; further economic and social development of the communities; and encourage sustainable use of natural resources. There is some funding available for management agreements in England and Wales for projects to meet local environmental circumstances and priorities. All national parks are run by National Park Authorities. In England and Wales funding is 75 per cent from the national government and 25 per cent from local authorities; in Scotland funding is entirely from the national government

58   Outside the National Parks are areas designated as AONB, or in Scotland, National Scenic Areas (NSA). AONBs cover an area of 24,511 km^2 and NSAs 10,018 km^2, in all over 14 per cent of the UK land area. Their designation is recognition of the national scenic and landscape importance of the area. The main means of protection is that AONB or NSA status has to be taken into account when the local planning authority deals with any planning application, balancing the national need with the designated status.

59   Taken together national parks, AONBs (England, Wales and Northern Ireland) and NSAs (Scotland) cover 21 per cent of the UK land area.

60   The Countryside Agency (CA) has nine land management initiatives, including one covering the Northumberland National Park and another part of the Peak District. Initiatives in the Humberhead Levels and Severn Valley are designed for water and flood management.

61   SSSIs are administered by English Nature, Scottish Natural Heritage and the Countryside Council for Wales with payments to farmers to protect and conserve the landscape, rare species, and biodiversity. In England they cover 6.3 per cent of the land and in Wales over 10 per cent. In Scotland over 12 per cent of the land area is in SSSIs. In Northern Ireland, Areas of Special Scientific Interest (ASSI) are similar and cover a total of 912 km^2, or 6.5 per cent. In the UK SSSIs and ASSIs account for 7.7 per cent of the total land area. Agri-environment agreements for Environmentally Sensitive Area (ESA) and stewardship schemes require the management of any SSSIs or ASSIs within the scheme area.

62   Other designated sites are for specific protection, some of which are of world wide importance such as Ramsar sites (wetlands) or World Heritage sites. Others include local and national nature and other reserves.

63   The National Trust and Scottish National Trust own a total of 3,230 km^2 in the UK. They aim to preserve the traditional character of the area with active farm management.

64   In 2002 the area of land designated in England as Nitrate Vulnerable Zones (NVZ) was increased from 5,710 km^2 (4.4 per cent) to 63,447 km^2 (49 per cent). NVZs protect ground and river waters by imposing mandatory limits on the use of fertilisers. Farmers in NVZs can apply for Farm Waste Grants; since 1996 £364,000 has been paid through the scheme.

65   Integrated Farm Management (IFM) is a whole-farm policy providing the basis for efficient and profitable production which is economically viable and environmentally responsible. IFM integrates beneficial biological processes into modern farming practices using advanced technology. This involves the consideration in agricultural organisation and planning of soil management and crop nutrition; crop protection; pollution control and waste management; energy efficiency; landscape and wildlife features, and animal husbandry. Agriculture Departments use demonstration farms and supply advice on management practice, including the use of manure. Linking Environment and Farming (LEAF) actively promotes IFM with a self-assessment audit and over 1,500 members now consider

IFM in their management decisions involving over 191,894 hectares.

66 In April 1993, 30,424 hectares on 849 holdings were registered as being farmed organically in the UK. By June 2002 this had increased to 699,879 hectares of land on 5,995 holdings. Emphasis is placed on maintaining healthy soil, and measures such as adequate rotations have to be taken to ensure its fertility and biological activity. Inputs into organic production are strictly regulated and the use of artificial fertilisers and pesticides is excluded. Conversion to organic farming systems provides gains in terms of soil health and fertility. Biodiversity benefits from the use of crop rotations, as well as the absence of synthetic pesticides, herbicides and fertilisers.

Rural development programmes - agri-environment and other schemes
(Tables 8.6 and 10.2)

67 Agri-environment schemes make payments to farmers for 5 to 10 year agreements for conservation matters. The Environmentally Sensitive Areas (ESA) Scheme was introduced in 1987 to offer incentives to farmers to adopt agricultural practices which would safeguard and enhance parts of the country of high landscape, wildlife or historic value. Outside ESA areas, Countryside Stewardship (England) together with Tir Gofal (Wales), Rural Stewardship (Scotland) and Countryside Management (Northern Ireland) aim to conserve traditional countryside landscapes and features; improve and extend wildlife habitats; conserve historic, geological and landscape features and restore traditional aspects of the countryside. They aim to make conservation part of management practice. These schemes are now managed under the Rural Development Programmes (RDP), together with organic conversion, farm woodlands and schemes for energy crops, rural enterprise, processing and marketing and vocational training. In England four areas have been chosen to pilot a new entry-level scheme to encourage more environmentally friendly farming.

68 Expenditure on these and other schemes under the RDP amounts to £3.1 billion over the lifetime of the programmes. The funding of these schemes comes jointly from the EU and the UK Government (see Chapter 9).

69 Table 8.6 shows expenditure on individual agri-environment schemes by country. Because individual schemes use different scheme years, data for each scheme is shown in the year in which the bulk of that scheme's payments were made. In 2002 expenditure on agri-environment schemes increased by 25 per cent, and organic conversion schemes by over 50 per cent. Expenditure on all non-product subsidies rose by 5.8 per cent even though set-aside payments fell by 15 per cent. Further information on the specific schemes can be found on the Defra, SEERAD, NAWARAD and DARD websites.

70 The area of land within agri-environment schemes continues to increase. Table 10.2 shows the area of land within individual schemes by country. The area shown for SSSIs, ASSIs and ESAs in table 10.2 is that for which there are payments for management schemes. SSSIs within ESA or stewardship management schemes, and receiving payments through those schemes, are included in tables 8.6 and 10.2 under ESA or other management scheme.

71 A report (McInerney et al, 2000) suggests that the farm-level costs for countryside maintenance and management averages £23 per hectare for areas outside agri-environment schemes. This is mainly spent on field boundaries but also on woodlands, traditional buildings, footpaths and semi-natural features such as ponds.

Table 10.1 Direct and indirect energy consumption

Inquiries: Barbara Norton on 01904 455577 email: barbara.norton@defra.gsi.gov.uk

PJ, Joules x 10^{15}

	1985	1990	1993	1995	1997	1999	2000	2001
Fuel								
Direct energy - total	59.3	56.3	57.1	58.1	56.8	50.4	48.6	48.9
Coal	0.3	0.5	0.3	0.4	0.2	0.1	0.1	0.1
Biomass	..	3.1	3.1	3.1	3.1	3.1	3.1	3.1
Natural gas	2.9	4.0	4.7	4.5	5.7	4.2	4.7	4.8
Electricity	14.4	13.9	13.8	14.2	13.7	14.0	16.3	16.5
Petroleum	41.7	34.8	35.2	35.9	34.1	29.0	24.4	24.4
Indirect Inputs								
Indirect Energy total	181.0	172.6	150.0	164.5	160.0	150.1	145.1	134.2
Fertiliser	133.8	128.8	104.6	115.8	113.8	109.7	107.5	94.6
Pesticide	10.6	10.1	10.3	9.8	10.3	9.5	8.2	8.6
Tractor purchases	15.0	11.4	12.8	14.6	12.3	9.5	9.3	10.3
Animal Feeds	21.6	22.2	22.2	24.2	23.6	21.4	20.2	20.7
Total Energy	240.3	228.9	207.1	222.6	216.8	200.5	193.7	183.1

Source : ADAS, Reports prepared for Defra using : Digest of UK Energy Statistics, Agriculture in the UK, Fertiliser Manufacturers Association, Agricultural Engineers Association, Crop Protection Association

Table 10.2 Environment schemes - land in schemes by country

Inquiries: Barbara Norton on 01904 455577 email: barbara.norton@defra.gsi.gov.uk

Thousand hectares   Scheme year

	1992	1994	1996	1998	2000	2001	2002
England							
Environmentally Sensitive Areas (a)	129.4	346.4	433.6	501.2	531.9	579.0	620.0
Countryside Stewardship	..	..	90.9	118.3	192.1	263.3	321.8
Arable Stewardship	..	..	..	..	2.0	2.0	2.0
Organic Conversion	..	1.6	4.7	10.7	95.9	137.9	158.3
Nitrate Sensitive Areas	9.2	13.0	23.4	27.9	9.6	5.8	4.8
Countryside Access	..	..	0.1	0.1	0.1	0.1	-
Habitat	..	3.7	6.7	6.0	7.1	7.1	7.1
Moorland	..	..	11.3	15.8	15.8	15.8	2.7
Woodland schemes	12.8	18.6	22.5	29.3	36.2	40.9	45.9
English Nature, SSSI (a)	..	..	..	..	..	..	128.0
Wales							
Environmentally Sensitive Areas (a)	..	15.4	33.4	62.0	70.7	..	..
Tir Cymen	..	..	..	..	88.6	..	..
Tir Gofal	..	..	..	..	50.0	..	..
Organic Conversion	..	..	..	..	34.2	..	..
Habitat	..	..	..	..	7.3	..	..
Moorland	..	..	..	..	0.6	..	..
Woodland schemes	..	0.2	0.5	0.7	0.7	..	..
Countryside Council for Wales, SSSI (a)	..	37.2	46.6	52.3	62.6	..	..
Scotland							
Environmentally Sensitive Areas (a)	120.6	149.6	374.1	515.3	771.7	771.1	..
Countryside Premium	..	..	..	..	..	..	
Rural Stewardship						..	..
Organic Conversion	..	..	16.5	23.2	212.3	232.7	..
Habitat and moorland schemes	..	..	0.1	0.5	1.6	3.8	..
Woodland schemes	..	..	..	..	..	..	..
Scottish Natural Heritage, SSSI (a)	..	..	..	246.0	287.0	312.0	332.0
Northern Ireland							
Environmentally Sensitive Areas (a)	..	..	117.9	144.8	154.3	147.6	143.2
Organic Conversion	..	..	..	0.5	1.0	3.8	4.6
Woodland schemes	..	207.5	250.0	416.1	2 039.2	1 520.4	1 582.7
Countryside Management	..	..	..	..	..	19.2	57.0
ASSI (a)	..	..	597.1	87.7	50.1	78.4	73.7

source: Defra website, www.defra.gov.uk/esg

(a) All land designated as Environmentally Sensitive Area (ESA), Site of Special Scientific Interest (SSSI) or Area of Special Scientific Interest (ASSI) does not necessarily receive management payments.

References

Carvalho L and Moss B. (1998) 'Lake SSSIs Subject to Eutrophication - an Environmental Audit', English Nature Freshwater Series, No. 3.

The Countryside Agency (2001) 'The State of the Countryside 2001: The National Report'.

Defra (2002a) 'The Environment in your Pocket 2002: Key Facts and Figures on the Environment in the UK', November.

Defra (2002b) 'Farming and Food's Contribution to Sustainable Development: Economic and Statistical Analysis, December, available online at www.defra.gov.uk/farm/sustain/newstrategy/index.htm.

Defra (2003) 'Digest of Environmental Statistics', February, available online at www.defra.gov.uk/environment/statistics/des/contents.htm.

English Nature (2002) 'The Role of Economic Instruments in Managing Diffuse Nutrient Pollution', No.462 English Nature Research Reports

Environment Agency (2002) 'Agriculture and Natural Resources: Benefits, Costs and Potential Solutions', May.

Hanley, N (2001) (ed), 'Estimating the Value of Environmental Features, a Report to MAFF, June, available online at www.defra.gov.uk/esg/econwork.htm.

Hartridge, O and Pearce, D. (2001) 'Is UK Agriculture Sustainable? Environmentally Adjusted Economic Accounts for UK Agriculture', CSERGE - Economics paper, September.

McInerney J P, Turner M M, Barr D and MacQueen, G. (2000) 'What's the Damage? A Study of Farm Level Costs in Managing and Maintaining the Countryside, Special Studies in Agricultural Economics, Report No. 51, December.

Pretty J, Brett C, Gee D, Hine R, Mason C F, Morison J I L, Raven H, Rayment M and van der Bijl G. (2000) 'An Assessment of the Total External Costs of UK Agriculture', Agricultural Systems Vol. 65 pp. 113-136.

Stewart L, Hanley N and Simpson I (1997) 'Economic valuation of agri-environment schemes in the United Kingdom', unpublished Report by the Environmental Economics Research Group, University of Stirling, to HM Treasury and MAFF.

Willis K G, Garrod G D and Saunders C M (1993) 'Valuation of the South Downs and Somerset Levels and Moors Environmentally Sensitive Area Landscapes by the General Public', a Report to MAFF by the Centre for Rural Economy, Department of Agricultural Economics and Food Marketing, University of Newcastle upon Tyne.

Glossary

Definitions of terms used in the production and income account.

Term	Table 6.1 ref.	Definition
Agricultural Industry		All activities taking place within businesses that carry out any agricultural activities. These businesses include all farms and specialist agricultural contractors.
Capital formation in livestock	9	Production of animals that will be used as the means of production, e.g. breeding animals.
Other agricultural activities	12	Agricultural activities that do not result in sales of final product, e.g. quota leasing, contract work.
Inseparable non-agricultural activities	13	Non-agricultural activities which are included within the business level accounts and are inseparable, e.g. some cases of bed and breakfast and recreation facilities.
Gross output at basic prices	14	Output including directly paid subsidies that are closely correlated with production of a specific product. The output of the agricultural industry includes some non-agricultural activities and transactions within the industry.
Basic prices		Market price plus directly paid subsidies that are closely correlated with production of a specific product
Subsidies (less taxes) on product	15	Subsidies and taxes on products are shown in detail in table 6.7; all subsidies are recorded on an as due basis
Intermediate consumption	26 (17-25)	Consumption of goods and services, e.g. feed, seeds, fertiliser, pesticides.
Gross value added (at basic prices)	27 (14-26)	Gross Output at basic prices less Intermediate Consumption.
Consumption of fixed capital	28	The reduction in value (at current prices) of capital assets used in the production process, e.g. buildings, plant, machinery, vehicles and livestock.
Net value added at basic prices	29 (27-28)	Gross Value Added at basic prices less Consumption of fixed capital.
Other Subsidies (less taxes) on production	32	Subsidies and taxes not closely correlated with production of a specific product, e.g. agri-environment payments, set-aside, animal disease compensation.
Net value added at factor cost	33	Net Value Added at basic prices plus other subsidies (less taxes) on production
Compensation of employees	30	The full costs of employees to the business including national insurance contributions.
Total Income from Farming (TIFF)	36	Income to those with an entrepreneurial interest in the agricultural industry, e.g. farmers, partners, spouses and most other family workers.

Further information

Additional information is available at:

ADAS	www.adas.co.uk
British Potato Council	www.potato.org.uk
British Trust for Ornithology	www.bto.org
Countryside Agency	www.countryside.gov.uk
Countryside Council for Wales	www.ccw.gov.uk
Defra	www.defra.gov.uk
Department of Agriculture and Rural Development (Northern Ireland)	www.dardni.gov.uk
England Rural Development Programme	www.defra.gov.uk/erdp
English Nature	www.english-nature.org.uk
Environment Agency	www.environment-agency.gov.uk
Eurostat	www.europa.eu.int/comm/eurostat
Forestry Commission	www.forestry.gov.uk
HM Customs and Excise	www.hmce.gov.uk
Home-Grown Cereals Authority	www.hgca.co.uk
Livestock and Meat Commission for Northern Ireland	www.lmcni.com
Meat and Livestock Commission	www.mlc.org.uk
National Assembly for Wales Agriculture and Rural Affairs Department	www.wales.gov.uk/subiagriculture
Office for National Statistics	www.statistics.gov.uk
Royal Society for the Protection of Birds	www.rspb.org
Rural Payments Agency	www.rpa.gov.uk
Scottish Agricultural College	www.sac.ac.uk
Scottish Executive Environment and Rural Affairs Department	www.scotland.gov.uk
Scottish Natural Heritage	www.snh.org.uk
Valuation and Lands Agency (NI)	http://vla.nics.gov.uk
Valuation Office Agency (GB)	www.voa.gov.uk

Related data is available on the Defra website at 'Economics/Statistics' under 'Publications' (www.defra.gov.uk/esg/m_publications.htm):

2002

National Statistics Year Ahead Programme: Defra National Statistics Publications

Publication dates and formats of Defra National Statistics publications.

June Agricultural Census Analyses (http://farmstats.defra.gov.uk)

A wide variety of detailed data covering England are available on the June Census web pages including the following:

- A query facility allowing selection of census data from regional down to ward level
- Frequency distribution tables for main census items
- Agricultural Atlas containing colour maps showing the distribution of main census items in England.
- Historical agricultural data covering the last 50 years available at county level for England.

Farm Incomes in the United Kingdom

Farm Incomes in the United Kingdom provides an authoritative and detailed source of information on the incomes and financial structure of the agricultural industry in each of the four countries of the United Kingdom.

Agricultural Market Reports

Prices and quantities sold of cereals, feedingstuffs, hay and straw, potatoes, livestock, finished stock and eggs and poultry; national average wholesale prices of home grown fruit, vegetables, flowers and pot plants.

Basic Horticultural Statistics

This publication provides comprehensive statistics for the United Kingdom horticulture industry. Each publication covers an 11 year period.

Digest of Environmental Statistics

This key reference document for environmental data information provides a handy tool to assist informed discussion of environmental policies and developments both in the UK and in the international arena.

United Kingdom Sea Fisheries Statistics

The *United Kingdom Sea Fisheries Statistics* provide a broad picture of the United Kingdom industry and its operations.

Family Food in 2001/02

Family Food in 2001/02 is due to be published in July 2003. This is an annual report on food consumption, expenditure and nutrient intakes. It compares households across demographic classes and includes trends over time. This is the first report based on the results of the Expenditure and Food Survey. Previous years' results are based on the old National Food Survey.'